# Superalloys

## Alloying and Performance

**Blaine Geddes**
**Hugo Leon**
**Xiao Huang**

ASM International®
Materials Park, Ohio 44073-0002
www.asminternational.org

First printing, November 2010

Great care is taken in the compilation and production of this book, but it should be made clear that NO WARRANTIES, EXPRESS OR IMPLIED, INCLUDING, WITHOUT LIMITATION, WARRANTIES OF MERCHANTABILITY OR FITNESS FOR A PARTICULAR PURPOSE, ARE GIVEN IN CONNECTION WITH THIS PUBLICATION. Although this information is believed to be accurate by ASM, ASM cannot guarantee that favorable results will be obtained from the use of this publication alone. This publication is intended for use by persons having technical skill, at their sole discretion and risk. Since the conditions of product or material use are outside of ASM's control, ASM assumes no liability or obligation in connection with any use of this information. No claim of any kind, whether as to products or information in this publication, and whether or not based on negligence, shall be greater in amount than the purchase price of this product or publication in respect of which damages are claimed. THE REMEDY HEREBY PROVIDED SHALL BE THE EXCLUSIVE AND SOLE REMEDY OF BUYER, AND IN NO EVENT SHALL EITHER PARTY BE LIABLE FOR SPECIAL, INDIRECT OR CONSEQUENTIAL DAMAGES WHETHER OR NOT CAUSED BY OR RESULTING FROM THE NEGLIGENCE OF SUCH PARTY. As with any material, evaluation of the material under end-use conditions prior to specification is essential. Therefore, specific testing under actual conditions is recommended.

Nothing contained in this book shall be construed as a grant of any right of manufacture, sale, use, or reproduction, in connection with any method, process, apparatus, product, composition, or system, whether or not covered by letters patent, copyright, or trademark, and nothing contained in this book shall be construed as a defense against any alleged infringement of letters patent, copyright, or trademark, or as a defense against liability for such infringement.

Comments, criticisms, and suggestions are invited, and should be forwarded to ASM International.

*Prepared under the direction of the ASM International Technical Book Committee (2009–2010), Michael J. Pfeifer, Chair.*

*ASM International staff who worked on this project include Scott Henry, Senior Manager, Content Development and Publishing; Steven R. Lampman, Content Developer; Eileen De Guire, Senior Content Developer; Ann Britton, Editorial Assistant; Bonnie Sanders, Manager of Production; Madrid Tramble, Senior Production Coordinator; Diane Whitelaw, Production Coordinator; and Patricia Conti, Production Coordinator.*

Library of Congress Control Number: 2010937091
ISBN-13: 978-1-61503-040-8
ISBN-10: 0-61503-040-9
SAN: 204-7586

ASM International®
Materials Park, OH 44073-0002
www.asminternational.org

Printed in the United States of America

# Contents

# List of Figures

# List of Tables

# Preface

Superalloys are among the most compositionally complex alloys ever developed, containing a multiplicity of alloying elements and producing multiple phases with important mechanical effects. A few key alloying elements produce the dominant phases, while a variety of adjunct elements, often in trace amounts, can modify the properties; in some cases, the modification is profound. The topic of superalloys is ripe for research, especially experimental research, and new effects, sometimes subtle, continue to be discovered.

The primary purpose of *Superalloys: Alloying and Performance* is to examine the role of alloying elements in superalloys, ultimately for understanding the suitability for a particular application. The main target audience for the book is mechanical, materials, and metallurgical engineers and technologists in industry involved in the design, specification, or application of superalloys. It would also be of interest to academia, where students and researchers may find it useful as a broad reference and succinct summary of research in the field. The book attempts to fill a niche for a concise, practical, readable summary of the topic of superalloys.

The book is quite descriptive, without mathematical rigor, and stands alone sufficiently for anyone with a basic knowledge of materials science to grasp. It is not envisioned to be a book of interest to the layman, but by virtue of its descriptive nature, the layman is not shut out. The book is accessible to anyone requiring a detailed knowledge of the chemistry, phases, and microstructure of superalloys.

The gas turbine engine, with its high temperatures and stresses, is the dominant application that drives the superalloy industry, continually demanding that the mechanical performance boundaries be advanced. The big metallurgical advances enabled the development of the jet aircraft. Minor metallurgical advances continue to gradually push the temperature envelope, enabling higher efficiencies and/or greater component longevity in the gas turbine engine. Other applications have arisen as the technology evolves, with the application base of superalloys now extending to such areas as nuclear reactors, biomedical devices, petrochemical equipment, and high-temperature furnaces.

The book presents an overview of the subject of superalloys and summarizes current research in the field. It discusses the phases present and the effect of many alloying elements on developing those phases and their effect on mechanical performance. Abundant citations to the references support the text. Few other books address the compositional effects on microstructure and mechanical properties so broadly. The book is not meant to be an exhaustive or deep discussion of the field; rather, the authors strived to produce a brief, focused summary that invites the reader with specific interests to consult more specialized works.

The economic importance of the gas turbine engine spurs continued research in the field. The dominant mode of research continues to be experimental because the metallurgical complexity of superalloys, coupled with the computational sophistication of accurate quantitative prediction of the behavior of such materials, renders theoretical investigation valuable only in the sense of gaining a cursory understanding. Accumulating the body of knowledge and detailed understanding of interrelated effects of many alloying elements, often in trace amounts, by experiment is slow, painstaking work and continues to be new research ground for the application of practical talents; hence, the field evolves slowly.

Blaine Geddes

CHAPTER **1**

# Introduction

THERE IS NO STRICT DEFINITION of a superalloy, although a commonly accepted one is that a superalloy is an alloy based on group VIII elements (nickel, cobalt, or iron with a high percentage of nickel added) to which a multiplicity of alloying elements are added. The defining feature of a superalloy is that it demonstrates a combination of relatively high mechanical strength and surface stability at high temperature (Ref 1).

The primary application that has driven superalloy development is for use as air foils in the hot section of gas turbine engines (GTEs), but they have been used successfully in other applications, such as rocket components, nuclear reactors, industrial furnaces, heat exchangers, petrochemical equipment, petroleum production equipment, automotive turbochargers, and biomedical devices.

Superalloys are among the most compositionally complex metallic alloys ever developed for commercial use. Their compositional complexity allows the development of a wide range of alloys that can be optimized through processing for specific applications. The need for materials with higher-temperature capability has driven superalloy development to the present level of sophistication. The high level of investment and the complexity of composition and processing make the cost of superalloys typically in the range of 30 to 200 times that of plain stainless steel (Ref 2).

Although there are a number of other material groups that can be used at high temperatures, such as ceramics and refractory metal alloys, superalloys are unsurpassed in terms of the combination of high-temperature mechanical properties and environmental resistance, as shown in Fig. 1.1, and are the primary choice for structural applications at high temperatures. Although ceramics have very good environmental resistance, their low fracture toughness makes them unsuitable for most structural applications. Refractory metal alloys retain their mechanical properties at higher temperature because of their high melting points, but they have poor oxidation

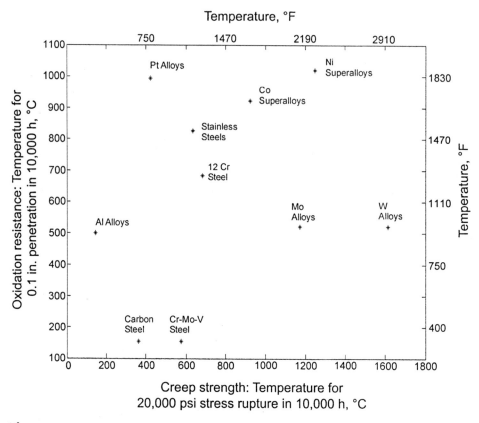

**Fig. 1.1** Environmental resistance and strength for various metallic families. Source: Ref 1

resistance. The combination of environmental resistance and superior mechanical properties at high temperatures sets superalloys apart from other alloy systems (Ref 1).

Simultaneously achieving optimal properties in any material is rarely possible, so a superalloy composition is often optimized for particular mechanical properties at the expense of oxidation/corrosion resistance or vice versa, or the properties represent a compromise, with manufacturability (castability, forgeability, weldability) and cost taken into account.

This review provides an overview of superalloys, strengthening mechanisms, and phases and also discusses the roles of alloying elements. Throughout the text, reference is made to numerous superalloys whose compositions are defined in Appendix A. Note that this is not a definitive list of superalloy compositions but merely a selection of some of the most notable alloys. Properties for each alloying element are included in Appendix B. The mechanical properties of selected superalloys are tabulated in Appendix C.

## 1.1 Historical Development

Superalloy development has been driven primarily by the need for materials that can withstand the increasing operating temperatures and stresses of components in GTEs. There is some debate as to who is the creator of the GTE, with some crediting Dr. Frank Stolze (1872), who filed a patent that described a device resembling the GTE, and others crediting Charles Curtis, who produced some working models in the early 1900s. Both Stolze's paper design and Curtis's working models had a common flaw, which was that the compressor required more power than the turbine could produce, therefore making them mechanical curiosities rather than useful devices.

The first self-sustaining GTE, unveiled in Paris in 1903, consisted of a three-cylinder reciprocating compressor and an impulse turbine. With a three percent thermal efficiency, it gave a humble start to the technology that today drives ships and airplanes and provides reliable electric generation. The Norwegian engineer Aegidus Elling later produced a GTE based on a centrifugal compressor and radial turbine that could produce 11 hp at a turbine inlet temperature of approximately 400 °C (750 °F) (Ref 3). This comparatively low temperature permitted the use of austenitic stainless steels as structural materials, which had been discovered in the 1910s and quickly became the first choice for high-temperature applications (Ref 1).

The development of GTE technology then started in earnest, with the General Electric company, in collaboration with the U.S. Army, starting a gas turbine division under the direction of Dr. Stanford A. Moss from Cornell University, which resulted in the General Electric turbosupercharger engine for aircraft use during World War I. This not only resulted in development of aerodynamic design but also of high-temperature materials. In approximately 1918, British patents were awarded for Nichrome, a Ni-20Cr alloy, which was a starting point for future superalloys (Nimonics, Inconels) (Ref 1, 4). In 1929, Bedford, Pilling, and Merica patented the addition of small amounts of titanium and aluminum to Nichrome (Nimonic 80) for increased strength. Not until after the invention of the electron microscope (1931) could Taylor and Floyd conduct their research and report in 1951 that it was the precipitation of the $\gamma'$ ($Ni_3Al$) phase that caused the higher strength that was the subject of the Bedford, Pilling, and Merica patent. By 1935, Elling had improved his GTE design to the point where it produced 75 hp yet had a turbine inlet temperature of 550 °C (1000 °F), which was still within the temperature capability of austenitic stainless steels. The need for superalloys was not realized until the development of the aircraft GTE.

The aircraft GTE was developed independently by Hans von Ohain and Max Hahn, working for an engineering firm called Ernest Heinkel in Germany, and at a similar time by Sir Frank Whittle, working in collaboration with the Royal Aircraft Establishment in England. The Heinkel engine He-178 was patented in 1935, five years after Whittle patented his engine, and in 1939 was the first GTE to successfully power an aircraft. Subsequently, Whittle had his first successful flight in 1941. This marked an important year for superalloy development because the turbine inlet temperature had risen to 780 °C (1450 °F), which precluded the use of conventional austenitic stainless steels. This led to the first use of superalloys in GTEs, represented by the wrought Rex-78, which was essentially a heavily modified or "super"-alloyed stainless steel (Ref 3).

The development of cobalt-base superalloys occurred at the same time as the introduction of the austenitic stainless steel-based superalloys. In the early 1900s, patents were issued for Co-Cr and Co-Cr-W systems developed for environmentally aggressive applications, such as cutlery, machine tools, and wear-resistant surfaces (Ref 5). By the time the United States had developed its first aircraft GTE in 1943, cobalt-base superalloys had been introduced, and Haynes Stellite 21 (a cast alloy intended primarily for dental implants) was chosen as the very first turbine blade material.

Most of the early nickel-iron- and cobalt-base alloys were strengthened by carbide dispersions, although Nimonic 80 did exhibit some precipitation hardening due to the formation of a $\gamma'$-Ni$_3$Al phase. In the late 1940s, molybdenum was introduced into alloy M-252, producing a significant amount of solid-solution strengthening and leading to a more widespread use of refractory metals in nickel-iron- and nickel-base superalloys (Ref 1). The next major step in superalloy development occurred around the 1950s, when Eiselstein introduced alloy 718, a superalloy strengthened by the $\gamma''$-Ni$_3$Nb precipitate.

The superalloy development from the 1930s to 1950s can be considered as being based on microstructure optimization. The next step in the history of superalloy development was characterized by process optimization. In 1952, Falih N. Darmara introduced commercial vacuum melting technology, with the first vacuum-melted alloys beginning to appear in approximately 1955. Both vacuum induction melting (VIM) and vacuum arc remelting allowed the charge to remain molten for longer periods of time, providing greater opportunity for complete degasification and removal of volatile impurities as well as for sampling and adjusting the composition of the melt. Vacuum induction melting also allowed more effective use of trace amounts of beneficial elements, such as boron, manganese, and silicon, as deoxidants, leading to improved high-temperature properties, especially ductility (Ref 6).

Although vacuum casting increased alloy performance by improved compositional control, the more significant effect of VIM was to allow much higher levels of aluminum and titanium to be added to the alloy, leading to the widespread development of $\gamma'$ precipitation-hardened nickel-base superalloys. Without vacuum melting and casting, these alloying elements would oxidize rapidly, negating their value as strengthening agents and rendering the alloys unfit for most structural applications.

Other superalloy derivatives, such as oxide-dispersion-strengthened (ODS) alloys and mechanically alloyed alloys, were developed at Dupont in 1965 and INCO in 1966, respectively. Later, starting in 1969, Pratt and Whitney Aircraft pioneered an entirely new field with the development of directionally solidified alloys for airfoils (Ref 7).

While the vacuum casting processes had opened the door to higher levels of alloying, the precipitation of detrimental phases and the subsequent loss of properties in superalloys during service revealed the need for compositional limits based on phase stability that were largely independent of the manufacturing process. The formation of detrimental phases was found to be associated with high chromium levels, which prompted a reduction of chromium levels in superalloys from approximately 20 to 10 weight percent. The reduction in chromium made the alloys vulnerable to hot corrosion, which was painfully evident in helicopter engines ingesting sea spray during the Vietnam War. Although chromium levels could not be increased without loss of mechanical properties, the environmental resistance of the low-chromium alloys was clearly unacceptable.

The solution was to use coatings for increased environmental resistance. Diffusion coatings were the first to be developed in which large amounts of principally aluminum were diffused into the surface of the substrate superalloy. These coatings proved to be highly successful because their increased oxidation and corrosion resistance permitted turbine inlet temperatures up to 1200 °C (2200 °F) (Ref 8). The first commercial application appeared during the late 1950s on cobalt-base first-stage turbine vanes. In the early to mid-1960s, this coating technology was applied to nickel-base superalloy turbine blades (Ref 9, 10). The topic of protective coatings was given much attention at the first conference dedicated to superalloys, which took place in 1968 at the Seven Springs Mountain Resort in Champion, Pennsylvania.

The other major class of turbine coatings, MCrAlY (where "M" is cobalt, nickel, iron, or nickel/cobalt), began its development in 1965, with the first application appearing in 1969 (Ref 11). The first patent for an MCrAlY coating on a nickel or cobalt substrate was awarded in 1970 to Talboom and Grafwallner (Ref 12) of United Aircraft Corporation, in which an FeCrAlY-type coating was proposed. It was later discovered that the poor stability of iron aluminide compounds, compared to nickel aluminide, caused rapid aluminum depletion in the coating by diffusion of aluminum to the coating/substrate interface (Ref 9). This determined the later development of MCrAlY coatings to be based on cobalt and nickel, such as CoCrAlY (Ref 13), NiCrAlY (Ref 14), and NiCoCrAlY (Ref 15).

By the 1970s, it was becoming evident that while superalloys with protective coatings had sufficient strength and creep resistance and adequate environmental resistance, the general failure mode had shifted to thermomechanical fatigue (TMF). This prompted a new generation of alloys that were optimized for improved TMF resistance through processing using techniques of directional solidification and powder metallurgy. The last major development in superalloy technology came about in 1979, when PWA-1480 became the first commercial single-crystal (SX) superalloy (Ref 7), which permitted higher creep life and temperature capability than had ever been achieved before. Since then, progress has continued toward the development of alloys containing rhenium and ruthenium and optimized for SX processing.

The path of future superalloy development is unclear. Single-crystal superalloys are reaching their temperature limits of 1200 °C (2200 °F), with incipient melting occurring in the vicinity of 1300 °C (2370 °F). Another class of superalloys, ODS superalloys, also reach their highest useful temperatures at 1200 °C (2200 °F) (Ref 4). With further increases in the turbine inlet temperature, researchers are now striving to find the next generation of materials, in combination with thermal barrier coatings, that will perform at even higher temperatures. More recently, the emphasis in new superalloy development is on cost reduction (replacement of ruthenium, for example) and improvements to SX casting yields in manufacturing (Ref 16).

## 1.2 Applications of Superalloys in the GTE

Because the driving force for superalloy development has been the demands of GTE applications, a review of superalloys commonly used in the engine is presented. It is important to note that not all superalloys have the same characteristics; each alloy is chosen, depending on the function of the component, for an optimal combination of manufacturability, cost, and mechanical, thermal, and environmental properties.

Superalloy applications in GTEs can generally be divided into two groups:

- *Stationary parts:* Includes combustor cans, nozzles, guide vanes, seals, and casings
- *Rotating parts:* Includes discs, shafts, blades, and spacers

The combustor endures the highest temperatures in the engine but carries limited structural loads, which makes creep and oxidation resistance among the main concerns when selecting the material. An additional consideration in combustor design is the complicated shape, which requires a number of sheet metal forming operations and joining methods. Superalloys such as Nimonic 75, Hastelloy X, Inconel 600, and Haynes 188 are commonly selected for this application because of their excellent formability and weldability.

The next major engine components are the turbine vanes, which see slightly lower temperatures than the combustor, but oxidation resistance is still a significant consideration. The difference in pressure on the airfoil surfaces also causes stresses that make creep resistance a key consideration in materials selection. One of the most common phenomena observed is the "bowing" of the airfoil due to creep deformation. Typical alloys selected for the vane assembly are Waspaloy, X-40, alloy 713, MAR-M 302, B-1900, and columnar-grained MAR-M 200.

Turbine blades are exposed to the hot gas stream and are subject to hot corrosion and oxidation in the same way as combustor and vane surfaces. Additionally, the turbine blades must withstand significant structural loads, caused by centrifugal and thermal stresses. Furthermore, the tips of the rotating blades must maintain very tight clearances with respect to the stationary components to improve engine efficiency, which means the alloy must be highly resistant to creep deformation. Another important issue is hot corrosion from the effect of salt deposits when sulfur, as a fuel impurity, reacts with airborne sea salts in a marine atmosphere to condense as sodium sulfate (Ref 17). Among the most notable blade alloys in the order of historical development are Udimet 500, Inconel 100, Udimet 700, Inconel 738, columnar-grained MAR-M 200, MAR-M 200 + Hf, PWA 1484, and CMSX 2.

Turbine disks are designed for high static strength, fatigue resistance, and toughness and do not experience temperatures as high as the turbine blades, which has led to widespread use of alloys such as Incoloy 901, Waspaloy, Astroloy, A-286, and Inconel 100. The desire for tight clearances throughout the engine gas path to decrease pressure losses has led to the development of low-thermal-expansion superalloys, such as Incoloy alloys 903, 907, 909, and (more recently) Inconel 783, for components requiring critical clearance, such as casings (Ref 1). The extreme temperatures in the engine impose stringent requirements even on the auxiliary components, with alloys such as MP35N, MP159, Inconel X750, and Inconel 751 being developed specifically for applications where stress relaxation is to be avoided (for example, bolts, springs, and other fasteners) (Ref 18).

## REFERENCES

1. C.T. Sims, Superalloys: Genesis and Character, *Superalloys II,* C.T. Sims, N.S. Stoloff, and W.C. Hagel, Ed., John Wiley & Sons, 1987, p 3–26
2. R.J. Quigg, Tantalum's Effect on Nickel-Base Superalloys, *Proc. International Symposium on Tantalum and Niobium,* Nov 1988, p 619–629
3. Energy Conversion, in Vol 18, *Encyclopedia Britannica,* 15th ed., 2002, p 332–413

4. M.J. Donachie and S.J. Donachie, *Superalloys: A Technical Guide*, 2nd ed., ASM International, 2002

5. M. Beltran, Cobalt-Base Alloys, *Superalloys II*, C.T. Sims, N.S. Stoloff, and W.C. Hagel, Ed., John Wiley & Sons, 1987, p 135–163

6. R.T. Holt and W. Wallace, Impurities and Trace Elements in Nickel-Base Superalloys, *Int. Met. Rev.*, Vol 21, 1976, p 1–14

7. J.M. Poole, J.J. Fischer, G.A.J. Hack, and G.M. McColvin, The Development, Performance and Future of the Mechanical Alloying Process and Oxide Dispersion Strengthened Alloys, *Advances in High Temperature Structural Materials and Protective Coatings*, A.K. Koul, Ed., National Research Council of Canada, Ottawa, 1994, p 34–53

8. "High-Temperature Oxidation-Resistant Coatings," National Research Council Committee on Coatings, National Academy of Sciences, Washington, D.C., 1970

9. G. Goward, Protective Coatings for High Temperature Alloys State of Technology, *Proc. Symposium on Properties of High Temperature Alloys, with Emphasis on Environmental Effects*, Vol 77 (No. 1), 1976, p 806–823

10. J. Nicholls, Designing Oxidation-Resistant Coatings, *JOM*, Vol 52 (No. 1), 2002, p 28–36

11. G. Goward and P. Sahoo, On the Suitability and Application of MCrAlY Coatings Under Various Operating Conditions, *Advances in Thermal Spray Science and Technology, Proc. Eighth National Thermal Spray Conference*, Sept 1995 (Houston, TX)

12. F. Talboom and J. Grafwallner, Nickel or Cobalt Base with a Coating Containing Iron, Chromium, and Aluminum, U.S. Patent 3,542,530, 1970

13. D. Evans and R. Elam, Cobalt Base Coating for the Superalloys, U.S. Patent 3,676,085, 1972

14. G. Goward, D. Boone, and F. Pettit, High-Temperature Oxidation-Resistant Coating Alloy, U.S. Patent 3,754,903, 1973

15. R. Hecht, G. Goward, and R. Elam, High Temperature NiCoCrAlY Coatings, U.S. Patent 3,928,026, 1975

16. S. Tin, Intelligent Alloy Design: Engineering Single Crystal Superalloys Amenable for Manufacture, *Mater. Sci. Technol.*, Vol 25 (No. 2), 2009, p 136–146

17. R. Rapp, Hot Corrosion of Materials, *Pure Appl. Chem.*, Vol 62 (No. 1), 1990, p 113–122

18. Y. Yamada and K. Toshio, *Materials for Springs*, Japan Society of Spring Engineers, Springer, 2007

CHAPTER **2**

# Overview of Superalloys

SUPERALLOYS ARE CLASSIFIED according to the main alloying elements in the composition, with the three base metals being nickel, cobalt, and iron. The entire superalloy family shares a common basic microstructure, which is a face-centered cubic (fcc) matrix with a number of dispersed secondary strengthening phases. In elemental form, nickel is the only superalloy base metal with an fcc structure at room temperature. Cobalt is hexagonally close-packed (hcp) at room temperature but undergoes a transformation to fcc at 417 °C (783 °F). Iron has a body-centered cubic (bcc) structure at room temperature but undergoes a phase transformation to fcc austenite at 912 °C (1674 °F). In superalloys, both iron and cobalt are stabilized by the addition of nickel to retain an fcc crystal structure throughout the gas turbine engine (GTE) application temperature range.

## 2.1 Nickel-Iron-Base Alloys

Nickel-iron-base superalloys are characterized by their high toughness and ductility and are used mostly in applications where these properties are required, such as turbine discs or forged rotors. Consequently, nickel-iron alloys are used only in the wrought condition (Ref 1), because this manufacturing method offers a wide variety of mechanisms for controlling grain size and morphology. In addition to their high toughness, another advantage of nickel-iron-base superalloys is their lower cost due to the substantial amount of iron added (Ref 1).

There are three groups of nickel-iron-base superalloys. The first is the precipitation-hardened alloys, where $\gamma'$-$Ni_3(Al,Ti)$ and/or $\gamma''$-$Ni_3Nb$ precipitates form in the fcc $\gamma$ matrix. The second is the low-coefficient-of-thermal-expansion (CTE) group of alloys discussed subsequently. The third group of nickel-iron-base superalloys is the modified stainless steels, primarily strengthened by solid-solution hardening and minor carbide precipitation, such as 19-9DL (18-8 stainless steel with slight chromium and nickel adjustments, additional solution hardeners, and higher carbon) and Inconel-800H (21% Cr and high nickel with small additions of titanium and aluminum, which produce some $\gamma'$ phase) (Ref 1). The field of stainless steels is broad; they are not strictly considered to be superalloys, and a stainless steels discussion is beyond the scope of this work.

### 2.1.1 Precipitation-Hardened Nickel-Iron Alloys

Among the alloys that are strengthened through $\gamma'$ precipitation are A-286, V-57, Nimonic 901, and Inconel 718. Unfortunately, $\gamma'$ precipitation only occurs at low levels of aluminum in nickel-iron-base alloys (further described in section 5.4, "Aluminum," in this book), which means that most nickel-iron-base superalloys rely on titanium additions for hardening through the precipitation of $\gamma'$-Ni$_3$Ti. Long-term exposure above 650 °C (1200 °F) tends to cause the $\gamma'$ to transform to coarse platelet $\eta$ phase (an hcp Ni$_3$Ti phase), which results in a considerable decrease in strength (Ref 2). Low levels of aluminum also decrease the environmental resistance of the alloy, because without sufficient aluminum, the alloy cannot form a protective alumina scale.

Another highly effective strengthening precipitate, body-centered tetragonal $\gamma''$-Ni$_3$Nb, forms in alloys that contain niobium. The most widely known such alloy is Inconel 718, a highly weldable superalloy, which accounts for 35 percent of total wrought superalloy production worldwide (Ref 3). It is used in aircraft GTE components such as the compressor and turbine discs, casings, compressor blades, and fasteners. Some alloys may contain combined aluminum, titanium, and niobium, which could result in dual strengthening by $\gamma'$ and $\gamma''$, as is the case with Inconel alloys 706, 709, and 718. These three alloys may be considered to be nickel base, but they have sufficiently high iron contents to be classified as nickel-iron-base superalloys.

### 2.1.2 Low-Thermal-Expansion Superalloys

For components such as shrouds and casings, a smaller CTE allows smaller clearances between rotating and nonrotating components, thus increasing overall engine efficiency (Ref 4). Not only do these alloys have a low CTE, but they also maintain it at a relatively constant value with rising temperatures (Ref 1), as shown in Fig. 2.1. Although nickel- and cobalt-base superalloys generally have lower CTEs than nickel-iron-base superalloys, the low-thermal-expansion superalloys, for example, Incoloy alloys 903, 907, and 909, Inconel 783, and Thermospan, achieve the lowest thermal expansion of all superalloys due to their carefully optimized compositions.

Low-thermal-expansion superalloys rely on the Invar effect to achieve their low thermal expansion. In these alloys, the contraction associated

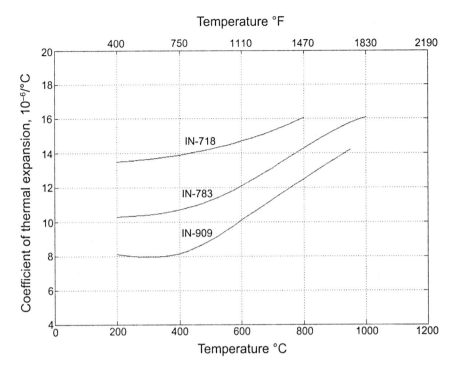

**Fig. 2.1** Mean coefficient of thermal expansion (CTE) between 25 °C (77 °F) and the temperature shown for a conventional nickel-base superalloy (Inconel 718), a conventional low-CTE superalloy (Incoloy 909), and a three-phase-strengthened low-CTE superalloy (Inconel 783). Source: Ref 5

with the loss of ferromagnetism on heating compensates normal thermal expansion. Thus, the expansion of the alloy is controlled by the changes in the alloy magnetic properties. The control of the magnetic properties is achieved through careful composition design. For example, the optimal composition for minimum thermal expansion over the 20 to 600 °C (68 to 1110 °F) temperature range corresponds to a nominal composition of 29Co-17Ni-Fe alloy (Ref 2). Note that this must be the residual composition of the matrix after solidification and does not take into account the quantity of these elements that may be tied up in secondary phases, such as the strengthening precipitates $\gamma'$ and $\gamma''$. Significantly, this composition is devoid of chromium, which is unusual for alloys that are intended for high-temperature applications. Chromium is avoided in these alloys because it strongly depresses the Curie point which is the phase-transformation temperature for the loss of ferromagnetism. Above the Curie point, the alloy exhibits paramagnetic behavior, and the thermal expansion is no longer counteracted by contraction due to loss of ferromagnetism. Therefore, the chromium content must be maintained as low as possible to achieve low thermal expansion at higher temperatures (Ref 6). Unfortunately, the low chromium content makes these alloys very sensitive to stress-assisted grain-boundary oxidation (SAGBO) embrittlement, which is one of the main drawbacks to their use (Ref 7).

The Ni-Fe-Co-base low-CTE superalloys are age hardenable through additions of aluminum, titanium, and niobium. Increased aluminum content is beneficial in the alloys for creep resistance and high-temperature stability (Ref 6). Inconel 783 is a low-expansion alloy that was developed to minimize general oxidation and SAGBO. Inconel 783 contains high aluminum levels (above five weight percent), which causes the precipitation of a $\beta$-aluminide phase (bcc-(Ni,Fe)Al) in addition to the $\gamma'$ strengthening phase. This alloy can be processed to offer good oxidation resistance while achieving low thermal expansion (Ref 7, 8) and improved stress-rupture characteristics (Ref 9).

The properties of the alloys with three-phase $\gamma$-$\gamma'$-$\beta$ microstructure, such as Inconel 783, depend on the ratios of nickel, iron, and cobalt. High-temperature ductility and stress-rupture properties are improved through increasing the cobalt-nickel ratio. Iron has a larger effect on the CTE as well as on high-temperature ductility and SAGBO due to the stabilizing effect on the $\beta$ phase.

## 2.2 Cobalt-Base Superalloys

Cobalt-base alloys are used for applications where hot corrosion is a major concern or for low-stress structural applications at moderate-to-high temperatures. Cast alloys are typified by X-40 and MAR-M 302, while Haynes 25 (L-605), Haynes 188, and S-816 are representative of wrought alloys. (Haynes 25 and S-816 are also available in cast form.) Typical applications for cobalt-base superalloys in GTEs are vanes and other stationary components, due to their superior stress-rupture properties and hot corrosion resistance. Cobalt-base superalloys can also be used to fabricate GTE blades but must be limited to lower stresses than nickel-base alloys.

Like all superalloys, the microstructures of cobalt-base superalloys consist of an fcc $\gamma$ matrix with a number of strengthening phases. However, the precipitation hardening in cobalt-base superalloys is not as effective as $\gamma'$ or $\gamma''$, as observed in nickel-iron- or nickel-base superalloys. This has made the cobalt-base superalloys heavily dependent on strengthening by carbide formation and solid-solution strengthening. An exception is J-1570, which derives some strengthening from $Ni_3Ti$ precipitation (Ref 1) but is not a competitive alternative to precipitation-hardened nickel-base superalloys.

The advantages of cobalt-base superalloys are (Ref 10):

- Higher melting temperatures (due to the higher melting point of cobalt) and correspondingly flatter stress-rupture curves, providing useful stress capability to a higher absolute temperature than polycrystalline nickel- or nickel-iron-base superalloys

- Superior hot corrosion resistance due to a higher chromium content
- Superior thermal fatigue resistance and weldability compared to nickel-base superalloys
- Limited amounts of aluminum and titanium permit the processing of cobalt-base superalloys by the use of air or argon melting, which is significantly less expensive than vacuum melting techniques.

Another very important group of cobalt-base superalloys is the wear-resistant alloys, such as Stellite 6B, but the poor ductility of these alloys limits them to use as coatings only.

## 2.3 Nickel-Base Superalloys

Nickel-base superalloys achieve the highest temperature/strength combination of all cast and wrought superalloys, making them ideal for the most demanding applications, such as turbine blades. Wrought nickel-base superalloys are often used where high toughness is required, such as turbine discs and forged blades. Examples of the wrought alloys include Udimet 700, Rene 41, Waspaloy, N-901, and Udimet 630. Castings are favored for high strength and creep resistance in high-temperature applications, such as investment-cast turbine blades and wheels, and are represented by alloys such as Inconel alloys 100, 713, 738, and 792, B-1900, and MAR-M 200 (Ref 11) and single-crystal cast alloys PWA1483, PWA1484, CMSX-4, and Rene N6.

The superior high-temperature capability of nickel-base superalloys is due to the precipitation of high volume fractions of the $\gamma'$-$Ni_3$(Al,Ti) phase, which requires combined aluminum and titanium contents of at least four to six weight percent. This precipitate is the main strengthening phase in such wrought alloys as Waspaloy, Astroloy, Udimet alloys 700 and 720 and in such cast alloys as Rene 80, MAR-M 247, and Inconel 713 and in all of the directionally solidified and single-crystal superalloys.

Some nickel-base alloys do not rely on precipitates for strengthening but rather depend mainly on solid-solution hardening (SSH). Two notable alloys strengthened by SSH are Hastelloy X and alloy 625, but they also derive some hardening through carbide and/or intermetallic compound precipitation.

Within the wrought alloys, there is another group of superalloys that is produced by pounding in a dry milling process. They are known as mechanically alloyed (MA) materials. The MA process involves a metallic and/or nonmetallic powder charge being worked by a highly energetic ball to produce a composite metal powder. As a result of the repeated welding-fracturing process, the MA powder has a fine lamellar structure (spacing under 0.7 μm) and is chemically homogeneous (Ref 12).

Mechanically alloyed materials exhibit improved high-temperature (up to 90 percent of melting point) strength through the combined effects of γ′ strengthening and fine oxide dispersions (Ref 12). The term *oxide-dispersion-strengthened (ODS) superalloys* is often used to describe MA materials containing oxide dispersions. Examples of ODS superalloys include Inconel alloys MA-754 and MA-6000E. It is important to note that the strengthening particles are added into the alloy during manufacturing and do not form (in this case, precipitate) from the alloy matrix, contrary to the way γ′, γ″, or carbides form. This oxide addition limits the manufacturing method of these alloys to mechanical alloying of powder materials and subsequent sintering and/or hot isostatic pressing. Melting of these alloys during processing cannot be tolerated, because the oxide particles would then segregate to the surface of the melt, due to their lower density, and leave the bottom of the casting depleted of the alloy principal strengthening phases.

Sometimes, powder metallurgy or isothermal forging is necessary to produce the wrought versions of such highly alloyed superalloys as Rene 95, Astroloy, and Inconel 100 due to their high volume fraction of γ′, which makes hot working of cast ingots difficult. Severe dendritic segregation, coarse grain size, and brittle interdendritic phases formed during solidification also make hot working difficult. Because of the high volume fraction of γ′ phase, there is a significant challenge in hot working due to the alloy high-temperature strength. When γ′ volume fractions are higher than 40 to 45 percent, the gap between the solvus and incipient melting temperature becomes too narrow for practical purposes and limits manufacturing methods to casting or powder metallurgy (Ref 2).

## REFERENCES

1. M.J. Donachie and S.J. Donachie, *Superalloys: A Technical Guide,* 2nd ed., ASM International, 2002
2. M. Durand-Charre, *The Microstructure of Superalloys,* Gordon and Breach Science Publishers, Amsterdam, 1997, p 1–124
3. J.A. Manriquez, P.L. Bretz, L. Rabenberg, and J.K. Tien, The High Temperature Stability of IN718 Derivative Alloys, *Superalloys 1992,* S.D. Antolovich et al., Ed., TMS, 1992, p 507–516
4. C.T. Sims, Superalloys: Genesis and Character, *Superalloys II,* C.T. Sims, N.S. Stoloff, and W.C. Hagel, Ed., John Wiley & Sons, 1987, p 3–26
5. Material Datasheets, Special Metals Corporation, 2004, http://www.specialmetals.com/products/
6. K.A. Heck, J.S. Smith, and R. Smith, Inconel 783: An Oxidation-Resistant, Low Expansion Superalloy for Gas Turbine Applications, *J. Eng. Gas Turbines Power,* Vol 120, 1998, p 363–369
7. R.J. Smith, G. Lewi, and D. Yates, Development and Application of Nickel Alloys in Aerospace Engineering, *Aircr. Eng. Aerosp. Technol.,* Vol 73 (No. 2), 2001, p 138–147

8. K.A. Heck and J.S. Smith, Inconel Alloy 783: An Oxidation-Resistant, Low Expansion Superalloy for Gas Turbine Applications, *J. Eng. Gas Turbines Power,* Vol 120 (No. 2), 1998, p 363

9. K.A. Heck, D.F. Smith, M.A. Holderby, and J.S. Smith, Three-Phase Controlled Expansion Superalloys with Oxidation Resistance, *Superalloys 1992,* S.D. Antolovich et al., Ed., TMS, 1992, p 217–226

10. A.M. Beltran, Cobalt-Base Alloys, *Superalloys II,* C.T. Sims, N.S. Stoloff, and W.C. Hagel, Ed., John Wiley & Sons, 1987, p 135–163

11. R.T. Holt and W. Wallace, Impurities and Trace Elements in Nickel-Base Superalloys, *Int. Met. Rev.,* Vol 21, 1976, p 1–14

12. J.M. Poole, J.J. Fischer, G.A.J. Hack, and G.M. McColvin, The Development, Performance and Future of the Mechanical Alloying Process and Oxide Dispersion Strengthened Alloys, *Advances in High Temperature Structural Materials and Protective Coatings,* A.K. Koul, Ed., National Research Council of Canada, Ottawa, 1994, p 34–53

CHAPTER **3**

# Strengthening Mechanisms

SUPERALLOYS ARE STRENGTHENED through three principal mechanisms: solid-solution hardening (SSH), precipitation hardening (PH), and dispersion strengthening. While grain size refinement could, in principle, provide an additional strengthening mechanism, it is rarely used due to the nature of the high-temperature environment. Cold working can be used but can only provide strengthening up to temperatures of approximately 540 °C (1000 °F) (Ref 1). While SSH, PH, and oxide and carbide dispersion strengthening can be present in the same alloy, there is usually one dominant mechanism. This is important for the component designer, because the strengthening mechanism plays a major role in the temperature/stress capabilities, manufacturing methods, and overall cost of the component.

Further improvement in mechanical properties, such as creep or stress-rupture resistance, is enabled by the control of the grain structure, as in columnar-grained alloys, or by the complete elimination of grain boundaries with the single-crystal superalloys.

## 3.1 Solid-Solution Hardening

Solid-solution hardening is the attainment of an increase in matrix strength by the addition of a different soluble element. The distortion of the atomic lattice caused by the misfit of atomic radius inhibits dislocation movement. Solid-solution hardening increases with atomic size difference, up to a maximum difference of approximately 10 percent in atomic size (Ref 2). The use of high-melting-point elements as the solutes provides stronger lattice cohesion and reduces diffusion, particularly at high temperatures. Similar considerations apply to the hardening of the $\gamma'$ phase.

Solid-solution hardening also has the effect of decreasing the stacking fault energy (SFE) in the crystal lattice, leading primarily to inhibition of dislocation cross slip, which is the main deformation mode in imperfect crystals at elevated temperatures (Ref 3). A lower SFE makes it more difficult for dislocations to change directions; thus, when a dislocation encounters a barrier, it is more difficult for the dislocation to be able to bypass that barrier by moving onto a new slip plane (Ref 1). In face-centered cubic (fcc) structures, the lowering of SFE leads to three interrelated effects:

- Dissociation of dislocations into partials
- Formation of hexagonally close-packed (hcp) stacking fault ribbons
- Increased difficulty of passage of dislocations from fcc matrix to hcp fault

Atomic clustering or short-range order is another mechanism that contributes to the strength obtained through solid solutions. The effect is related to electronic orbitals and is observed more strongly for certain elements, including molybdenum, tungsten, chromium, aluminum, and rhenium, that produce an enhanced hardening effect in a nickel matrix compared with iron, titanium, cobalt, or vanadium (Ref 2). The influence of the clustering effect has been observed in rhenium-modified CMSX-2 by atom probe microanalysis, showing small rhenium atom clusters of approximately 1 nm in size, which significantly impede dislocation movement and thereby improve alloy strength. Strengthening due to short-range order generally decreases rapidly above approximately 60 percent of the absolute melting temperature ($0.6T_M$) due to increased diffusion.

At temperatures above approximately $0.6T_M$, creep and strength are strongly influenced by diffusion, which greatly affects SSH alloys, as illustrated in Fig. 3.1 and 3.2. Generally speaking, SSH only provides strengthening up to approximately 815 °C (1500 °F) (Ref 5). Typical elements used in SSH of superalloys are aluminum, iron, titanium, chromium, tungsten, and molybdenum. The use of the more massive elements is desirable because of their lower diffusion rates, but they also increase alloy density and tend to promote the formation of topologically close-packed phases (discussed in section 4.8, "Topologically Close-Packed Phases," in this book).

## 3.2 Precipitation Hardening

A considerable increase in the creep strength of alloys for high-temperature applications can be obtained by PH. In the case of nickel-base alloys, this can be achieved using elemental additions such as titanium, aluminum, and niobium. These elements have limited solubility in the alloy matrix, and the solubility is drastically reduced with a decrease in

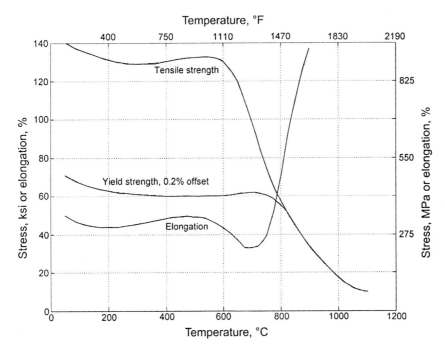

**Fig. 3.1** Tensile properties of solid-solution-hardened Inconel 625. Source: Ref 4

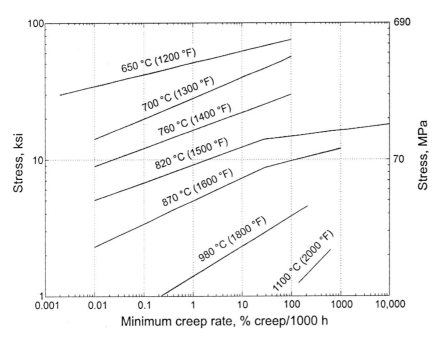

**Fig. 3.2** Creep strength of solid-solution-hardened Inconel 625. Source: Ref 4

temperature; therefore, finely distributed precipitates can be generated in the matrix from a supersaturated solid solution during heat treatment. The precipitates, which are generally coherent intermetallic compounds such as $\gamma'$-Ni$_3$(Ti,Al) or $\gamma''$-Ni$_3$Nb phase, can inhibit the movement of dislocations. Movement of a dislocation in the matrix containing precipitates can only take place by cutting through or by bypassing the particles.

The four main factors controlling the effectiveness of PH are (Ref 1, 5):

- Coherency strains between the matrix ($\gamma$) and the precipitate ($\gamma'$, $\gamma''$) due to the difference in their lattice parameters
- Antiphase-boundary (APB) energy in the presence of an ordered precipitate ($\gamma'$, $\gamma''$). The APB represents the energy needed for the dislocation to cut through the ordered precipitate, because cutting could result in disordering between the matrix and precipitate.
- Volume fraction of the precipitate ($\gamma'$, $\gamma''$)
- Particle size

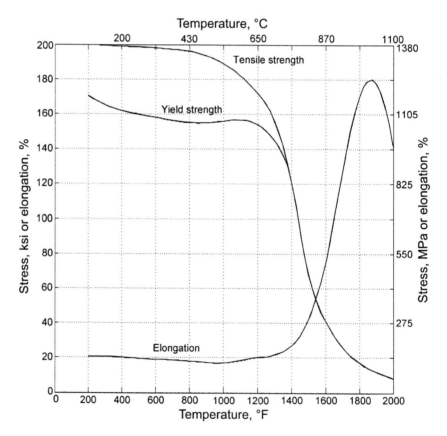

**Fig. 3.3** Mechanical properties of solid-solution-hardened and aged Inconel 718. Source: Ref 4

Note that the strengthening achieved through coherent strains and ordering increases with particle size, because these two mechanisms require that dislocations cut through the particle. However, this increase in strength with increasing particle size is limited by Orowan bowing (Ref 6), where the dislocation will bypass the particle if it is too large. The strengthening in this case is provided by the extra work needed for the dislocation to alter its path (Ref 5).

The morphology of the coherent precipitate in two-phase alloys is strongly influenced both by the elastic strain energy associated with the lattice mismatch between precipitate and matrix and by the interfacial energy of the particle-to-matrix boundary (Ref 7). The elastic strain energy depends on the shape, habit, and volume of the precipitates. Interfacial energy merely depends on the surface area of the particle. For a matrix and precipitate with similar lattice parameters, a spherical precipitate is formed, while for large differences in lattice parameters, an elastically favored cuboidal precipitate is formed. Figure 4.2 in Chapter 4 of this book shows a great diversity of $\gamma'$ morphology in various alloys under various heat treatments.

Precipitation-hardened alloys exhibit mechanical property changes in the vicinity of the solvus temperature of the strengthening precipitate. As can be seen in Fig. 3.3, the mechanical properties for Inconel 718 experience changes at approximately 700 °C (1300 °F), which is the solvus temperature for this alloy (Ref 1). Creep rates and stress rupture are likewise affected by precipitate dissolution.

## 3.3 Oxide Dispersion Strengthening

Oxide dispersion strengthening (ODS) is a mechanism similar to PH, except that the strengthening agent is added to the alloy and not precipitated from the matrix. In ODS, oxide particles act in a similar way to $\gamma'$ intermetallics by blocking dislocation motion, although the mechanisms are different because the particle is not coherent with the matrix. Unfortunately, the production of ODS alloys is complicated by the fact that the density of ceramics is lower than the metal matrix. The ceramic particles tend to float to the surface of the molten metal during casting (and welding), thus diminishing the strengthening effect. Therefore, ODS alloys are often fabricated by a combination of mechanical alloying, powder metallurgy, and subsequent thermomechanical processing.

Dispersions such as oxides are always incoherent with respect to the matrix (unlike precipitates formed within the alloy). Therefore, oxide additions only cause strengthening through the Orowan bypassing mechanism. Grain-boundary strengtheners as well as SSH are also usually incorporated in mechanically alloyed (MA) alloys, for example, Inconel MA-760 and Inconel MA-6000. Both precipitates and dispersions may be found in the same alloy, and hardening mechanisms are additive (Ref 8).

The particles in MA alloys are typically yttria and are fine and relatively uniformly dispersed, with a size on the order of 10 to 50 nm and interparticle spacings of 50 to 300 nm. Thoria was used as the dispersoid in an early ODS superalloy, but because thoria is radioactive, its use has been supplanted by yttria.

Another important factor is the grain aspect ratio (GAR), the ratio of grain length to width. Secondary recrystallization through zone annealing may be used to produce an elongated grain structure (Ref 9). A high GAR has been found to improve stress-rupture life (stress applied longitudinally), as shown in Fig. 3.4. With a high GAR and stress applied along the long axis of the grains, the number of transverse grain boundaries available to act as crack initiation sites is greatly reduced relative to an equiaxed grain structure.

Oxide-dispersion-strengthened alloys are ideal for very high-temperature applications for two reasons. One is that the oxide dispersion provides strengthening up to temperatures as high as 1300 °C (2370 °F) (Ref 10). The other is that the microstructure produced by consolidation of the MA powder through hot extrusion can be modified by thermal treatments and zone annealing to produce a highly anisotropic, coarse-grained structure with a GAR close to 100, which provides better creep resistance.

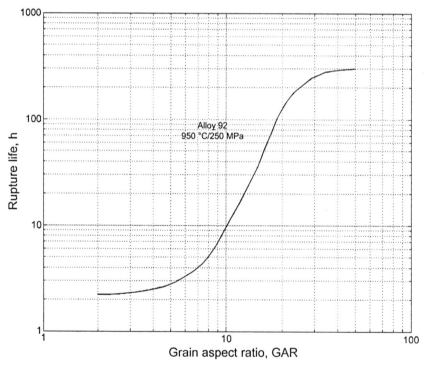

**Fig. 3.4** Stress-rupture life as a function of grain aspect ratio for Inconel 92 at 950 °C (1740 °F) and 250 MPa (36 ksi). Source: Ref 9

While ODS alloys can achieve the best strengths at the highest temperature of any superalloy (Ref 10), their widespread use is limited by the lack of intermediate-temperature stress-rupture strength, caused by the incoherent oxide particles. This is somewhat compensated by some $\gamma'$ strengthening, as in MA 6000, which permits the alloy to retain strength in two different temperature regimes.

## 3.4 Carbide Hardening

In alloy systems in which SSH elements such as molybdenum and tungsten have limited solubility, carbides are often used to provide high-temperature strengthening (Ref 3). Carefully designed carbide hardening can be particularly useful for increasing creep strength, because under service loads, the high-temperature creep processes mainly take place at the grain boundaries. Carbides, precipitated preferentially at the grain boundaries, inhibit grain-boundary slip, transferring creep processes from the grain boundary to the interior of the grain, where diffusion is slower. Small, globular, noncohesive carbides are best suited for stabilizing the grain boundaries. The primary carbides assume the formula of MC and $M_6C$, with "M" representing molybdenum, tungsten, titanium, and niobium. With prolonged exposure to high temperatures, MC and $M_6C$ carbides tend to transform to $M_{23}C_6$, as do chromium carbides. Because most high-temperature alloys contain high chromium contents for corrosion resistance, the formation of $Cr_{23}C_6$ carbides is unavoidable in alloys with carbon. The formation of chromium carbides depletes the surrounding matrix of chromium, reducing the corrosion resistance of the grain-boundary region, similar to the sensitization phenomenon in stainless steel.

The $M_{23}C_6$-type carbides are often cohesive and form along grain boundaries. Because carbides are brittle, these cohesive grain-boundary precipitates represent a preferred path for crack growth, resulting in a decrease in stress-rupture strength and ductility. In contrast, with noncohesive globular carbides, stresses can be reduced by slight grain-boundary slip, hindering or preventing the formation of microcracks. At high temperatures, $M_{23}C_6$ carbides also tend to agglomerate, forming fewer but larger carbides on the grain boundary, which could provide crack initiation sites (Ref 3). Figure 4.7 in Chapter 4 of this book shows a sampling of carbide morphology in various alloys.

The carbide-forming elements molybdenum and tungsten can be consumed as carbides at the grain boundaries after long-term exposure to high temperatures. This causes the grain-boundary zones to be depleted of these elements in the solid solution. While there is a disadvantage associated with the formation of such a depletion zone, the beneficial influence prevails, because the stresses can be dissipated via these "softer" zones adjacent to the grain boundaries and not through the carbide-rich grain boundaries. Improved creep-rupture strength has been observed due to this solid-solution depletion effect. Carbides can also provide strengthening in the same way as precipitates when they occur within the grain, but their main effect is when they occur as intergranular deposits and act to prevent grain-boundary sliding; thus, they improve creep resistance (Ref 11).

## REFERENCES

1. M.J. Donachie and S.J. Donachie, *Superalloys: A Technical Guide,* 2nd ed., ASM International, 2002
2. M. Durand-Charre, *The Microstructure of Superalloys,* Gordon and Breach Science Publishers, Amsterdam, 1997, p 1–124
3. P. Kumar, The Role of Niobium and Tantalum in Superalloys, *Advances in High Temperature Structural Materials and Protective Coatings,* A.K. Koul, Ed., National Research Council of Canada, Ottawa, 1994, p 34–53
4. Material Datasheets, Special Metals Corporation, 2004, http://www.specialmetals.com/products/
5. N.S. Stoloff, Fundamentals of Strengthening, *Superalloys II,* C.T. Sims, N.S. Stoloff, and W.C. Hagel, Ed., John Wiley & Sons, 1987, p 61–96
6. E. Orowan, in *Dislocations in Metals,* M. Cohen, Ed., AIME, New York, 1954
7. H.S. Ko, K.W. Paik, L.J. Park, Y.G. Kim, and J.H. Tundermann, Influence of Rhenium on the Microstructures and Mechanical Properties of a Mechanically Alloyed Oxide Dispersion-Strengthened Nickel-Base Superalloy, *J. Mater. Sci.,* Vol 33, 1998, p 3361–3370
8. J. Davis, *Nickel, Cobalt, and Their Alloys, ASM Specialty Handbook,* ASM International, 2000
9. L.J. Park, H.J. Ryu, S.H. Hong, and Y.G. Kim, Microstructure and Mechanical Behavior of Mechanically Alloyed ODS Ni-Base Superalloy for Aerospace Gas Turbine Application, *Adv. Perform. Mater.,* Vol 5, 1998, p 279–290
10. M.F. Hupalo, M. Terada, A.M. Kliaugua, and A.F. Padilha, Microstructural Characterization of Incoloy Alloy MA 956, *Mater.wiss Werkst.tech.,* Vol 34, 2003, p 505–508
11. F. T. Furillo, J. Davidson, and J. Tien, The Effects of Grain Boundary Carbides on the Creep and Back Stress of a Nickel-Base Superalloy, *Mater. Sci. Eng.,* Vol 39, 1979, p 267–273

CHAPTER **4**

# Phases and Microstructure of Superalloys

THE MICROSTRUCTURE OF SUPERALLOYS is highly complex, with a large number of dispersed intermetallics and other phases that modify alloy behavior through their composition, morphology, and location. This chapter gives an overview of the notable phases in superalloys and briefly describes how the microstructure can be modified through different processing methods, mainly heat treatments and directional solidification.

The microstructure of a superalloy can be described as a face-centered cubic (fcc) γ-phase matrix that contains a number of secondary phases. These secondary phases include fcc carbides, ordered fcc γ′, ordered body-centered tetragonal (bct) γ″, ordered hexagonal η, ordered orthorhombic intermetallic compounds, and many others, although not all phases are present in all superalloys. A summary of all of the major superalloy phases is presented in Table 4.1. As may be seen from the table, some phases in superalloys are beneficial and others degrade alloy properties (Ref 1).

The morphology of the precipitates is a key factor that determines the properties of the alloy. Continuous grain-boundary carbides render the alloy prone to brittle intergranular fracture; dispersed carbides along the grain boundaries pin the grains against sliding, thus increasing alloy strength. Because maximum strength is achieved with one particular γ′ precipitate morphology, but maximum stress-rupture strength is attained with a different morphology, most γ′-strengthened nickel-base superalloys have a bimodal γ′ morphology. The primary process that modifies precipitate morphology is heat treatment, which can occur deliberately in manufacture or inadvertently in service. The evolution of superalloy microstruc-

## Table 4.1 Phases observed in superalloys

| Phase | Crystal structure | Lattice parameter, nm | Formula | Comments |
|---|---|---|---|---|
| $\gamma$ | Face-centered cubic (fcc) | Depends on base metal | ... | Solid solution of the alloy elements in the base metal |
| $\gamma'$ | fcc (ordered $L1_2$) | 0.3561 for pure $Ni_3Al$ to 0.3568 for $Ni_3(Al_{0.5}Ti_{0.5})$ | $Ni_3Al$ $Ni_3(Al,Ti)$ | Principal strengthening phase in many Ni- and Ni-Fe-base superalloys; crystal lattice varies slightly (0–0.5%) from that of austenite matrix; shape varies from spherical to cuboidal; size varies with exposure time and temperature. $\gamma'$ is spherical in Ni-Fe-base and in some of the older Ni-base alloys, such as Nimonic 80 and Waspaloy. In more recently developed Ni-base alloys, $\gamma'$ is generally cuboidal. Experiments have shown that variations in Mo content and in the Al/Ti ratio can change the morphology of $\gamma'$. With increasing $\gamma/\gamma'$ mismatch, the shape changes in the following order: spherical, globular, blocky, cuboidal. When the $\gamma/\gamma'$ lattice mismatch is high, extended exposure above 700 °C (1290 °F) causes undesirable $\eta$ ($Ni_3Ti$) or $\delta$ ($Ni_3Nb$) phases to form. |
| $\eta$ | Hexagonally close-packed (hcp) ($D0_{24}$) | $a_o = 0.5093$ $c_o = 0.8276$ | $Ni_3Ti$ (no solubility for other elements) | Found in Ni-Fe-, Co-, and Ni-base superalloys with high Ti/Al ratios after extended exposure; may form as intergranular precipitates or intragranular acicular platelets in a Widmanstätten pattern |
| $\gamma''$ | Body-centered tetragonal (ordered $D0_{22}$) | $a_o = 0.3624$ $c_o = 0.7406$ | $Ni_3Nb$ | Principal strengthening phase in IN-718. $\gamma''$ precipitates are coherent disk-shaped particles that form on the {1 0 0} planes (average diameter approximately 600 Å, thickness approximately 50–90 Å). Upon overaging, $\gamma''$ transforms to $\delta$. |
| $\delta$ ($Ni_3Nb$) | Orthorhombic (ordered $Cu_3Ti$) | $a_o = 0.3624–0.511$ $b_o = 0.421–0.4251$ $c_o = 0.452–0.4556$ | $Ni_3Nb$ | Observed in overaged IN-718; has an acicular shape when formed between 815 and 980 °C (1500 and 1800 °F). Intergranular precipitate that impacts creep response |
| MC | Cubic | $a_o = 0.430–0.470$ | TiC NbC HfC | MC has some solubility for Ni, Zr, and Mo; appears as globular, irregularly shaped particles; "M" can be Ti, Ta, Nb, Hf, Th, or Zr. |
| $M_{23}C_6$ | fcc | $a_o = 1.050–1.070$ (varies with composition) | $Cr_{23}C_6$ $(Cr, Fe, W, Mo)_{23}C_6$ | Form of precipitation is important for mechanical properties; it can precipitate as globules, platelets, or lamellae; usually forms at grain boundaries; "M" element is usually Cr, but Ni, Co, Fe, Mo, and W can substitute. |
| $M_6C$ | fcc | $a_o = 1.085–1.175$ | $Fe_3Mo_3C$ $Fe_3W_3C$ $Fe_4W_2C$ $Fe_3Nb_3C$ $Nb_3Co_3C$ $Ta_3Co_3C$ | Randomly distributed carbide; "M" is generally Mo or W; there is some solubility for Cr, Ni, Nb, Ta, and Co. |
| $M_7C_3$ | Hexagonal | $a_o = 1.398$ $c_o = 0.4523$ | $Cr_7C_3$ | Generally observed as a blocky intergranular shape; observed in alloys such as Nimonic 80A after exposure above 1000 °C (1830 °F) and in some Co-base alloys |
| $M_3B_2$ | Tetragonal | $a_o = 0.560–0.620$ $c_o = 0.300–0.330$ | $Ta_3B_2$ $V_3B_2$ $Nb_3B_2(Mo, Ti, Cr, Ni, Fe_3B_2)$ $Mo_2FeB_2$ | Observed in Ni-Fe- and Ni-base alloys with approximately 0.03% B or greater; borides appear similar to carbides; "M" elements can be Mo, Ta, Nb, Ni, Fe, or V. |
| MN | Cubic | $a_o = 0.4240$ | TiN (Ti, Nb, Zr)N (Ti, Nb, Zr)(C, N) ZrN NbN | Nitrides are observed in alloys containing Ti, Nb, or Zr; they are insoluble at temperatures below the melting point; easily recognized as polished, having square to rectangular shapes, and ranging from yellow to orange. They often serve as nucleation sites for carbides. |
| $\mu$ | Rhombohedral | $a_o = 0.475$ $c_o = 2.577$ | $Co_2W_6$ $(Fe, Co)_7(Mo, W)_6$ | Generally observed in alloys with high levels of Mo or W; appear as coarse, irregular Widmanstätten platelets; form at high temperatures |
| Laves | Hexagonal | $a_o = 0.475–0.495$ $c_o = 0.770–0.815$ | $Fe_2Nb$ $Fe_2Ti$ $Fe_2Mo$ $Fe_2Ta$ $Fe_2Ti$ | Most common in Fe- and Co-base superalloys; usually appear as irregularly shaped globules, often elongated, or as platelets after extended high-temperature exposure |

(continued)

Source: Ref 1, 2

## Table 4.1 (continued)

| Phase | Crystal structure | Lattice parameter, nm | Formula | Comments |
|---|---|---|---|---|
| σ | Tetragonal | $a_o = 0.880$–$0.910$ <br> $c_o = 0.450$–$0.480$ | FeCr <br> FeCrMo <br> CrFeMoNi <br> CrCo <br> CrNiMo | Most often observed in Ni-Fe- and Co-base superalloys, less common in Ni-base alloys; appear as irregularly shaped globules, often elongated; form after extended exposure between 540 and 980 °C (1000 and 1800 °F). Needles or plates often in Widmanstätten form |
| $M_2SC$ | hcp | $a_o = 0.3234$–$3.386$ <br> $c_o = 11.233$–$11.834$ | $(Zr,Ti,Nb)_2SC$ | Observed at high levels of S or low C/S ratios |

Source: Ref 1, 2

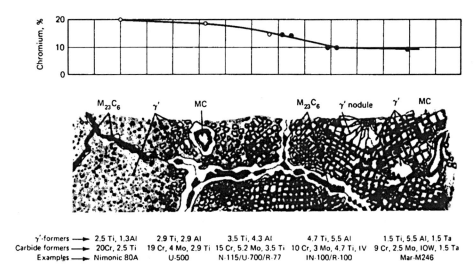

| | | | | | |
|---|---|---|---|---|---|
| γ'-formers ⟶ | 2.5 Ti, 1.3 Al | 2.9 Ti, 2.9 Al | 3.5 Ti, 4.3 Al | 4.7 Ti, 5.5 Al | 1.5 Ti, 5.5 Al, 1.5 Ta |
| Carbide formers ⟶ | 20 Cr, 2.5 Ti | 19 Cr, 4 Mo, 2.9 Ti | 15 Cr, 5.2 Mo, 3.5 Ti | 10 Cr, 3 Mo, 4.7 Ti, IV | 9 Cr, 2.5 Mo, IOW, 1.5 Ta |
| Examples ⟶ | Nimonic 80A | U-500 | N-115/U-700/R-77 | IN-100/R-100 | Mar-M246 |

**Fig. 4.1** Evolution of microstructure and chromium content of selected nickel-base superalloys. Desirable phases are highlighted in the microstructure. Source: Ref 3

tures, including the morphology of beneficial phases, is shown in Fig. 4.1 (Ref 3).

Grain sizes in superalloys are highly dependent on the manufacturing method. Grain sizes of ASTM 12 can be obtained in nickel-base gas turbine disc alloys made through powder metallurgy, whereas sheet metal and forgings typically have grain sizes between ASTM 4 and 6. Grain sizes in cast alloys are typically relatively large (ASTM 0 or greater) but not well controlled and are highly variable (Ref 1). Table 4.2 shows how the ASTM grain size number correlates to measured average grain size.

In the 1980s, Howmet Turbine Component Corporation pioneered Grainex, a fine-grained casting technique that uses agitation during solidification to break growing dendrites (branched treelike structures of crystals formed during solidification) and promote nucleation. Howmet then developed the Microcast-X process, which involves pouring at a temperature only slightly higher than the liquidus. Because the pour is turbulent

**Table 4.2 Correlation of ASTM grain size numbers to average grain size diameter**

The ASTM grain size number, n, is defined by the equation $N = 2^{n-1}$, where $N$ is the average number of grains per square inch at 100x magnification.

| ASTM No. | Average diameter, μm | Relative size |
|---|---|---|
| −1 | 510 | Very coarse |
| 0 | 360 | |
| 1 | 250 | Coarse |
| 2 | 180 | |
| 3 | 125 | |
| 4 | 90 | Medium |
| 5 | 65 | |
| 6 | 45 | |
| 7 | 32 | Fine |
| 8 | 22 | |
| 9 | 16 | |
| 10 | 11 | Very fine |
| 11 | 8.0 | |
| 12 | 5.6 | |
| 13 | 4.0 | Ultrafine |
| 14 | 2.8 | |
| 15 | 2.0 | |

and the pouring temperature is low, the alloy solidifies rapidly, producing a uniformly fine-grained casting with a cellular structure, rather than a dendritic structure, and an ASTM grain size in the three to five range. Similar grain sizes to those produced using Microcast-X have been demonstrated using intermetallic inoculants (Ref 4).

## 4.1 Matrix Phase

The fcc γ-phase matrix is ideal for high-temperature structural alloys for several reasons:

- The fcc matrix has optimal mechanical properties (tensile, rupture, creep, thermomechanical fatigue) because it has a high modulus and multiple slip systems (Ref 5).
- The densely packed fcc matrix is ideal for use at high relative temperatures ($T/T_M$) because of the low diffusivity of alloying elements (Ref 5, 6).
- The fcc matrix has a broad solubility of secondary elements that permits precipitation of intermetallic compounds, such as γ′ and γ″ for strengthening, and allows the dissolution of high-melting-point refractories (Ref 5).

The main element present in the matrix-phase composition is the superalloy base metal, but there is also a high percentage of solid-solution elements, such as cobalt (or nickel in the cobalt-base superalloys), chromium, molybdenum, tungsten, tantalum, and rhenium (Ref 7), which provide solid-solution hardening to the matrix.

# 4.2 Geometrically Close-Packed Phases

Geometrically close-packed (gcp) phases are intermetallics with the formula $A_3B$. They include the principal strengthening phases $\gamma'$ (fcc $Ni_3Al$, $Ni_3Ti$) and $\gamma''$ (bct $Ni_3Nb$) and the closely related $\eta$ (hexagonally close-packed $Ni_3Ti$) and $\delta$ (orthorhombic $Ni_3Nb$) phases. The $\gamma'$ phase is the most stable of the gcp phases and is the dominant strengthening phase in superalloys. The $\gamma''$ phase is exploited for strengthening in, for example, alloy 718.

The detrimental topologically close-packed (tcp) phases are also intermetallics, but they are discussed separately in section 4.8, "Topologically Close-Packed Phases," in this chapter. The gcp phases are close-packed in all directions, unlike the tcp phases, which have regular layered interruptions in their close-packed structure.

## 4.2.1 $\gamma'$-$Ni_3(Al,Ti)$

The $\gamma'$-$Ni_3(Al,Ti)$ precipitate is undoubtedly the most useful and important strengthening phase in superalloys. Its yield strength increases with temperature up to 800 °C (1470 °F), and it is the main strengthening constituent in a wide variety of nickel- and nickel-iron-base superalloys. It is metastable in nickel-iron-base alloys and will transform to $\eta$ over time in service at high temperature, which is a drawback to the use of iron as a base element.

Pure $Ni_3Al$ is a superlattice possessing the $Cu_3Au$ ($L1_2$)-type structure. It exhibits a long-range ordered structure up to temperatures near its melting point of 1385 °C (2525 °F). It exists over a fairly limited compositional range, but alloying elements may substitute liberally for either of its constituents to a considerable degree and thereby modify the phase properties. Most nickel-base alloys are strengthened by a $\gamma'$ precipitate in which titanium and/or niobium can substitute for up to 60 percent of the aluminum (Ref 8). Aluminum and titanium are the main alloying additions used to promote the precipitation of $\gamma'$.

The phase forms as a coherent precipitate within the $\gamma$ matrix, with morphologies dependent on heat treatment and exact composition. Some of the most representative morphologies are shown in Fig. 4.2 (Ref 9). Generally, $\gamma'$ disperses throughout the $\gamma$ matrix, but filmlike $\gamma'$ can also be formed along the grain boundaries after high-temperature exposure and is believed to be beneficial to creep-rupture properties (Ref 6, 7).

The coherence between the $\gamma'$ phase and fcc $\gamma$ matrix is maintained by tetragonal distortion (Ref 7). As a result, the nucleation of homogeneous precipitates with low surface energy and extraordinary long-time stability is possible. The presence of such precipitates is particularly useful in alloys intended for high-temperature exposure, because it allows the desired microstructure to be retained for a longer time at high temperatures.

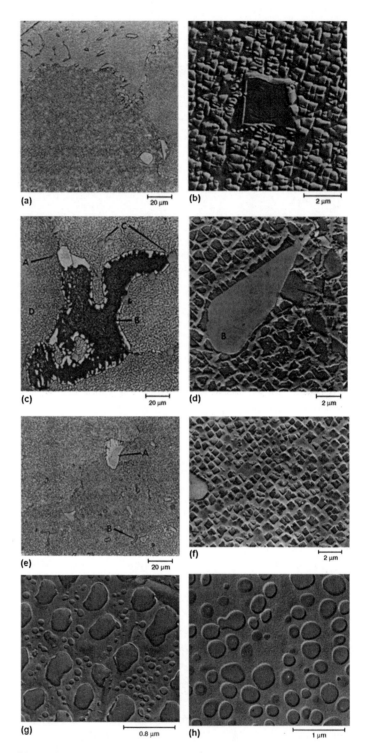

**Fig. 4.2** Selected morphologies of the γ′ phase. (a) B-1900 nickel-base alloy, as cast. Light-etching carbide particles are dispersed and at grain boundaries. The fine constituent within grains is γ′. (b) B-1900 nickel-base alloy, as cast. Replica electron micrograph showing large metal carbide particle and particles of γ′ in the γ matrix. (c) IN-100 nickel-base alloy, as cast. Light constituent (A) is primary (eutectic) γ′; dark (B) is probably perovskite, Ni₃(Al,Ti)C. Dispersed carbide particles are shown at C. Gamma matrix contains precipitated γ′ (D). (d) IN-100 nickel-base alloy, as cast. Replica electron micrograph showing islands of primary γ′ (A), a large particle of primary carbide (B), and dispersed particles of precipitated γ′ in γ matrix. (e) IN-738 nickel-base alloy, as cast. Structure consists of primary (eutectic) γ′ islands (shown at A), dispersed carbide particles (shown at B), and precipitated γ′ in the matrix of γ solid solution. (f) IN-738 nickel-base alloy, as cast. Replica electron micrograph showing randomly distributed precipitated γ′ Ni₃(Al,Ti) and a carbide particle (at left edge) in a matrix of γ solid solution. (g) IN-738 nickel-base alloy, solution annealed 2 h at 1120 °C (2050 °F), held 24 h at 845 °C (1550 °F). Replica electron micrograph of γ′ particles in γ; the smaller particles formed in cooling. (h) IN-738 nickel-base alloy casting, after holding at 815 °C (1500 °F) for 1000 h. Replica electron micrograph showing structure consisting of rounded γ′ particles in γ matrix. Source: Ref 9

The compatibility between $\gamma$ and $\gamma'$ is quantified by the lattice mismatch $\delta$:

$$\delta = \frac{\alpha_{\gamma'} - \alpha_{\gamma}}{\left(\dfrac{\alpha_{\gamma'} + \alpha_{\gamma}}{2}\right)}$$

(Eq 4.1)

The lattice mismatch is an important factor in determining the morphology of the $\gamma'$ precipitate (Fig. 4.3). A lattice mismatch magnitude between 0 and 0.2 percent produces a spherical precipitate; between 0.5 and 1.0 percent, a cuboidal precipitate; above 1.25 percent, a platelike precipitate (Ref 7). The spherical shape minimizes surface energy, but as the lattice mismatch grows larger, the change to cuboidal morphology is driven by the need to minimize elastic energy (Ref 11). The lattice parameter of the $\gamma$ matrix increases more rapidly with increasing temperature than the lattice parameter of the $\gamma'$ precipitate, and as a result, there is an increasingly negative lattice mismatch at elevated temperatures where creep is an issue (Ref 12).

The increased lattice mismatch between $\gamma/\gamma'$ improves creep life in single-crystal nickel-base superalloys (Ref 12), because the $\gamma/\gamma'$ interface is a barrier to mobile dislocations and a hindrance to plate thickening (see section "4.10 Rafting," in this chapter) due to dislocation pile-up at the interface. As the lattice mismatch is further increased, the interfacial dislocations become more closely spaced and act as a strong barrier to mobile dislocations shearing through the interface. It follows that for alloys with

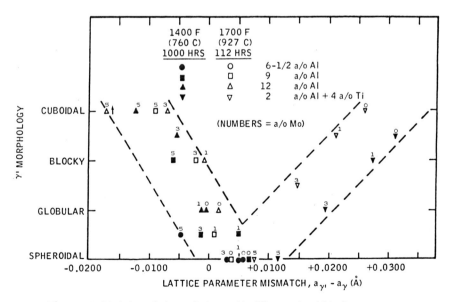

**Fig. 4.3** Variation of $\gamma'$ morphology with difference in $\gamma/\gamma'$ lattice parameter mismatch. Note that this graph does not plot $\delta$ along the x-axis.
Source: Ref 10

high values of lattice mismatch, the number of interfaces should be maximized to attain optimal properties. Alloys with lower values of lattice mismatch have weaker interfaces, and in these alloys, the number of interfaces appears to have less effect on creep properties.

The size of the $\gamma'$ precipitate is also important in providing effective precipitation hardening, because the hardening generally increases with particle size until the particle reaches a critical size. Beyond this size, the dislocation movement mode changes from a cutting mode to a bypassing mode, causing a loss of hardness and strength. This phenomenon can be clearly seen in Fig. 4.4, which shows hardness versus mean particle diameter at constant volume fraction of $\gamma'$ for an alloy with relatively low $\gamma'$ volume fraction, for example, A-286, Incoloy 901, and Waspaloy (Ref 1).

The shape and size of the $\gamma'$ precipitate can be modified through a coarsening process that takes place more rapidly at higher aging temperatures (Ref 13). At temperatures above approximately $0.6T_M$, $\gamma'$ ripens (increases in size) at a significant rate, facilitating dislocation bypassing. Measures that minimize ripening will help retain long-time creep resistance (Ref 7).

One of the most significant features of the $\gamma'$ phase is that its yield strength increases with temperature in the range of $-196$ to $800\ °C$ ($-320$ to $1470\ °F$). The relationship between yield strength and temperature is also highly dependent on the aluminum content in the $\gamma'$ phase, with the magnitude and position of the peak in flow stress being controlled by the presence of such other alloying elements as titanium, chromium, and niobium (Ref 8), as shown in Fig. 4.5. Both chromium and titanium raise the temperature of the flow-stress peak, but chromium weakens $\gamma'$ at low temperatures while titanium strengthens it. Ultimately, some high-temperature strength limit exists where the $\gamma'$ phase begins to dissolve.

The volume fraction of the $\gamma'$ phase is important for determining the strength and creep properties of the alloy and for determining the manu-

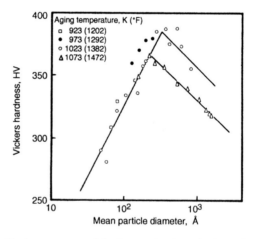

**Fig. 4.4**  Hardness versus particle diameter in a low-$\gamma'$-volume-fraction nickel-base superalloy. Source: Ref 1

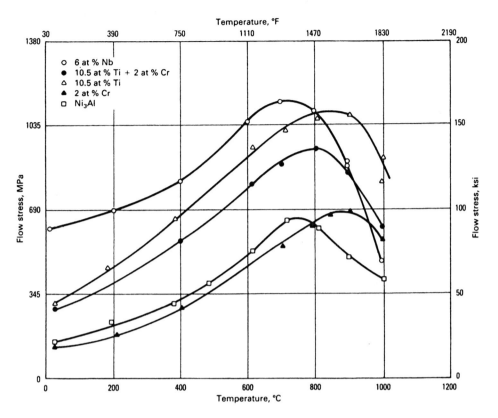

**Fig. 4.5** Variation of γ' peak flow stress with alloying additions. Source: Ref 1

facturing processes that can be used to produce a particular component. Although alloys can be hot worked at low γ' volume fractions, beyond 40 to 45 percent volume fraction of γ' (60 percent in the case of powder materials), forging is no longer practical, and the component must be manufactured by casting (Ref 14).

The disadvantage of γ'-strengthened alloys is that the service temperature and life of the component are ultimately limited by the coarsening and dissolution of the γ' precipitates. The binary nickel-aluminum phase diagram shows that complete dissolution of the phase occurs at approximately 1400 °C (2550 °F). However, in practice, much lower solvus temperatures for γ' are observed (Table 4.2) because of the effect of other elements in the alloy. Moreover, as the γ' solvus temperature approaches the alloy incipient melting point, heat treating of γ' precipitation-hardened alloys becomes more challenging.

### 4.2.2 γ''-Ni₃Nb

Very little information is available with regard to the γ''-Ni₃Nb phase. Although not as commonly used as the γ' precipitate, the γ'' precipitate is a useful strengthening phase, mainly in such nickel-iron-base superalloys as alloys 718 and 706. The $\gamma''$ precipitate is a coherent bct $Ni_3Nb$ phase with an ordered $D0_{22}$ crystal structure that assumes a disk-shaped morphology.

One of the main disadvantages of $\gamma''$ as a strengthening phase in comparison to $\gamma'$ is its lower solvus temperature. Alloys hardened through $\gamma''$ precipitation (notably alloy 718) have a rapid decrease in strength above 650 °C (1200 °F) (Ref 18), caused by the loss of the strengthening $\gamma''$ phase as it transforms to $\delta$. Nickel-iron-base alloys are particularly susceptible to the transformation of $\gamma''$ to $\delta$ at temperatures above 650 °C (1200 °F).

## 4.3 Carbides

The role of carbides in superalloys is complex; they can either increase or decrease alloy properties, depending on location, composition, and shape. Carbides are present in all superalloy families and tend to locate at grain boundaries, especially in nickel-base superalloys. However, in cobalt- and nickel-iron-base superalloys, intragranular carbides are commonly observed. In general, carbides provide a beneficial effect on rupture strength at high temperature if present in the right type (composition) and morphology (Ref 8). The shape of carbides also plays a role in alloy ductility. Indirectly, carbides adversely affect the chemical stability of their matrix by locally depleting carbide-forming elements (Ref 7).

Cobalt-base superalloys are primarily strengthened through carbide precipitation because they are not precipitation hardened by intermetallic compounds. In wrought cobalt-base alloys, where carbon contents are as high as 0.15 weight percent, carbides also control grain size during forging, heat treatment, and service exposure (Ref 19).

Primary carbides, for example, MC (where "M" is tantalum, titanium, zirconium, or tungsten), are formed as discrete blocky particles or as eutectic phases during casting solidification and commonly have an fcc crystal structure. These carbides form during solidification, occurring as discrete particles distributed heterogeneously throughout the alloy, at both intragranular and intergranular locations, and often form between dendrites. Little or no orientation relationship with the alloy matrix has been observed. These carbides act as a major source of carbon for the alloy during heat treatment and service (Ref 7). The preferred order of carbide formation in superalloys is as follows: HfC, TaC, NbC, and TiC in order of decreasing stability (which differs from the thermodynamic order: HfC, TiC, TaC, and NbC) (Fig. 4.6) (Ref 7, 20).

Secondary chromium-rich $M_7C_3$ and $M_{23}C_6$ carbides form mainly on the grain boundaries (Fig. 4.7) and usually occur as irregular, discontinuous, blocky particles, although plates and regular geometric forms have also been observed (Ref 22). The $M_6C$ carbides also precipitate in blocky form on grain boundaries and can form Widmanstätten structures. Examples of

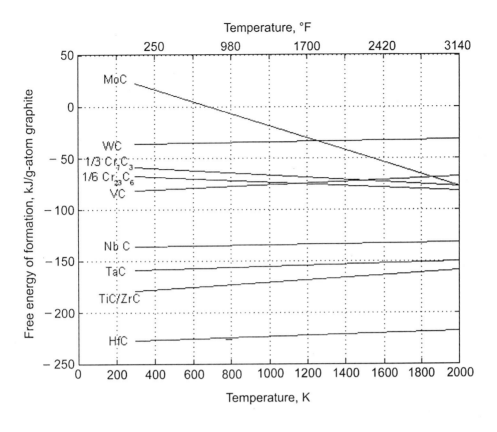

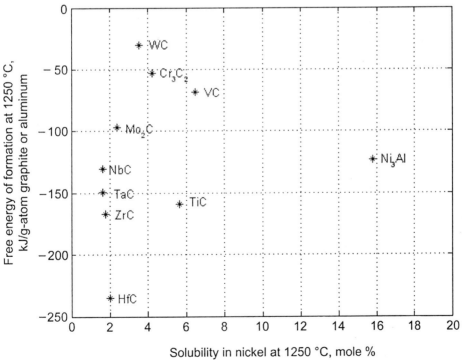

**Fig. 4.6** Standard Gibbs free energy of formation for several carbides as a function of (a) temperature and (b) solubility in nickel at 1250 °C (2280 °F). Source: Ref 21

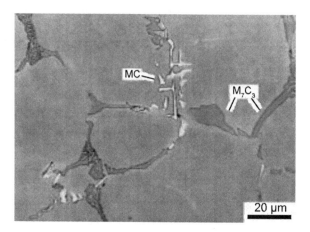

**Fig. 4.7** Scanning electron micrograph showing carbide distribution in an as-cast cobalt-base superalloy. Source: Ref 22

carbide distributions in a number of alloying systems are shown in Fig. 4.8 (Ref 9).

The $M_{23}C_6$ carbides are profuse in alloys with moderate to high chromium content and are the most common secondary carbides in cobalt-base superalloys, present in alloys from such early-generation superalloys as X-40 to modern MAR-M509 (Ref 22). They form at lower temperatures of 760 to 980 °C (1400 to 1800 °F) than $M_6C$ carbides; however, both types of carbides can form from the degeneration of MC carbides or from soluble residual carbon in the alloy matrix (Ref 24). They usually form on grain boundaries, but they can also form along twin boundaries, along stacking faults, and at twin ends (the "zipper" structure), as shown in Fig. 4.9. This phase displays a complex cubic structure, which, if the carbon atoms were removed, would closely approximate the structure of the tcp σ phase. Consequently, coherence between $M_{23}C_6$ and the σ phase is very high, and σ plates can often nucleate at $M_{23}C_6$ particles. The critical location of $M_{23}C_6$ along grain boundaries imparts a significant increase of stress-rupture strength, apparently through inhibition of grain-boundary sliding. Rupture failure can eventually initiate either by fracture of these grain-boundary carbides or by loss of cohesion at the $M_{23}C_6$ interface.

The $M_6C$ carbides also have a complex cubic structure but form at slightly higher temperatures of 815 to 980 °C (1500 to 1800 °F) than $M_{23}C_6$ carbides. They tend to be rich in such refractory elements as molybdenum and tungsten. Although similar to $M_{23}C_6$, they require higher molybdenum + tungsten content to form in nickel-base superalloys (6 to 8 atomic percent) (Ref 7) and cobalt-base superalloys (4 to 6 atomic percent) (Ref 22). In alloys with molybdenum plus tungsten content below these levels, $M_6C$ carbide formation can be induced if the decomposition of primary tungsten-rich MC carbides produces tungsten-rich zones. Because of their

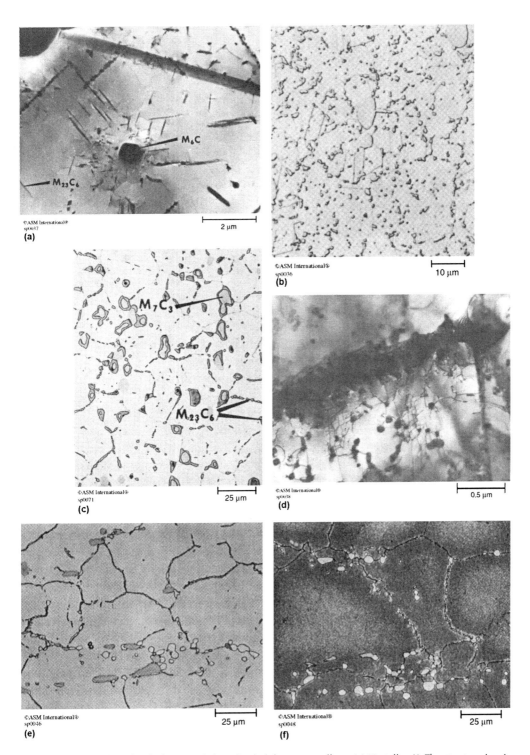

**Fig. 4.8** Examples of carbides in nickel- and cobalt-base superalloys. (a) Hastelloy X. The structure is primary $M_6C$ and needle-like $M_{23}C_6$ carbides that have precipitated at dislocations generated around primary carbide. The matrix is $\gamma$ solid solution. (b) Hastelloy X. Mixed carbide particles in a $\gamma$ matrix. (c) Stellite 6B. Dark areas around primary $M_7C_3$ show it changing to $M_{23}C_6$. (d) Hastelloy X. Structure is a bond of high dislocation density and precipitated $M_{23}C_6$ carbide at sites of high dislocation density and adjacent locations. (e) Rene 41. Stringers of carbide in a $\gamma$ solid-solution matrix. (f) Rene 41. Particles of $M_6C$ (white), metal carbide (gray), and $M_{23}C_6$ (at grain boundaries). Grain-boundary borders are darkened by $\gamma'$. Source: Ref 23

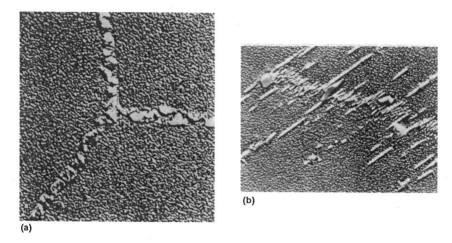

**Fig. 4.9** (a) Favorable discrete grain-boundary $M_{23}C_6$ at 10,000× and (b) less favorable discontinuous zipperlike precipitation at 6800× in Waspaloy. Source: Ref 1

higher formation temperature in comparison to that of $M_{23}C_6$, $M_6C$ carbides are more beneficial as a grain-boundary precipitate for controlling grain size during processing of wrought alloys (Ref 7). Carbides also provide microstructural refinement during cooling from heat treatment and during fabrication (Ref 6).

The mechanical properties most directly affected by carbides are stress-rupture strength and tensile strength, although the latter is a secondary consideration in nickel-iron- and nickel-base superalloys. The main benefit of primary MC carbides is indirect in that they provide a relatively stable source of carbon for precipitation of secondary carbides. However, scriptlike grain-boundary primary MC carbides serve both as crack initiation sites and crack propagation paths (Ref 20) and are therefore considered detrimental.

In most superalloys, it is the secondary carbides, formed during heat treatment, that provide significant beneficial effects, with the fine secondary carbide dispersions pinning dislocations and hardening the alloy (Ref 22). These carbides stabilize the grain boundaries against excessive shear and thereby improve stress-rupture strength. The amount of carbide at the grain boundaries must be precisely controlled, because continuous carbides at the grain boundaries provide easy paths for crack propagation, while lack of carbides means grains are free to slide against each other, reducing rupture life. In particular, cellular $M_{23}C_6$ and Widmanstätten-patterned $M_6C$ have been observed to reduce ductility and rupture life (Ref 20).

Carbide dispersions are sometimes thought to reduce alloy incipient melting temperature, but this is an indirect effect. The reduced melting temperature is due to the higher carbon contents necessary to form the carbides. When carbide dispersions are formed through mechanical alloying and not precipitation, the incipient melting temperature is observed to increase, not directly because of the carbides but because of the manufacturing method, which allows residual carbon concentration to be reduced (Ref 21). The disadvantage of adding carbide dispersions through mechanical alloying is the loss of coherency with the $\gamma$ matrix, which results in lower strengthening effects than would otherwise be achievable. For example, the dendritic structure of a cast alloy cannot exist in a mechanically alloyed material.

Carbides can have some effect on environmental resistance in the same way in which stainless steels are "sensitized." Because $M_{23}C_6$ and $M_6C$ carbides contain large amounts of chromium, it is believed that the areas around these carbides are locally depleted of chromium and act as initiation zones for stress-corrosion cracking (Ref 20).

## 4.4 Borides

Borides are hard refractory particles, with shapes varying from blocky to half-moon. They are found primarily at grain boundaries because boron, as a result of its small atomic radius and consequently low solubility in the matrix phase, tends to concentrate (and therefore to precipitate) at grain boundaries.

Borides can be used to strengthen nickel-iron- and nickel-base alloys (Ref 1) in a similar manner to carbides; they can also improve the hot workability of an alloy. Complex borides tend to have high molybdenum, titanium, chromium, and nickel contents and a tetragonal crystal structure in one of two forms. The first is a low-lattice-parameter eutectic product $MM'_2B_2$, where M and M' are respectively large- (molybdenum, titanium) and small- (chromium, nickel, cobalt) radius elements; the second is a high-lattice-parameter $M_2M'B_2$ spheroidal form. The first can be converted to the second by annealing below the solidus temperature (Ref 2).

Even though boron content is strictly controlled in new-generation superalloys, borides are observed in brazed joints of superalloys when low-melting-point Ni-Cr-B brazing alloys are used (Ref 25). Boron can contribute to cracking of the heat-affected zone in the welding of nickel-base superalloys even in concentrations of only a few parts per million (Ref 2, 7).

## 4.5 Oxides

Although surface oxides play a major role in the environmental resistance of an alloy, it is primarily in oxide-dispersion-strengthened (ODS) superalloys that oxides are present throughout by design. The first ODS superalloys relied on $ThO_2$ for strengthening. Today, the most common strengthening oxide in ODS superalloys is $Y_2O_3$, which, in alloys containing aluminum, reacts with it and forms mixed (yttrium, aluminum) oxide particles in the final alloy microstructure (Ref 26). In alloys containing hafnium, the formation of (yttrium, hafnium) oxides has been observed (Ref 21). The formation of orthorhombic $AlYO_3$ (yttrium-aluminum perovskite) and tetragonal $Y_3Al_5O_{12}$ (yttrium-aluminum garnet) has been observed in the ferritic alloy MA-956 and is shown in Fig. 4.10. Subsequent to thermal exposure at 750 to 850 °C (1380 to 1560 °F) for 1000 h, MA-956 is susceptible to embrittlement at 475 °C (890 °F) because of the formation of a coherent chromium-rich precipitate (Ref 26).

## 4.6 Nitrides

The most common nitride in superalloys is TiN; others include HfN and NbN. All of them appear as yellowish or orange small particles. Nitrides

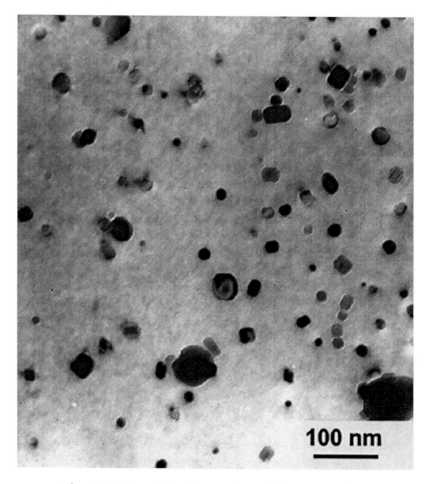

**Fig. 4.10** Transmission electron micrograph showing mixed (yttrium, aluminum) oxide particles dispersed in a ferritic matrix in MA-956. Source: Ref 26

form in the liquid phase just prior to solidification. They can act as nucleation sites both for primary MC carbides and for grains (tending to produce equiaxed grains); therefore, they are detrimental in directionally solidified alloys (Ref 27). However, because they are usually present in such small amounts, they are not believed to have any major influence on mechanical properties (Ref 28). They are insoluble to the melting point of the alloy and thus are not affected by heat treatment (Ref 28).

Work by Dahm et al. (Ref 29) has demonstrated that nitriding the surface of alloy 601 at temperatures from 350 to 525 °C (660 to 980 °F) using nitrogen plasma immersion ion implantation can produce dramatic increases in surface hardness and wear resistance, with some increase in corrosion resistance. Hardness was shown to increase by as much as five times, and wear resistance improved by as much as three orders of magnitude. In contrast to what occurs in stainless steels, the formation of CrN at the surface does not diminish the corrosion resistance of the alloy. Similar results have been independently obtained on alloy 718 using a similar technique known as plasma-assisted processing, where a nitrided surface layer of approximately 4 μm has been demonstrated to increase microhardness by about four times and to improve both wear resistance and corrosion resistance significantly (Ref 30).

## 4.7 Sulfocarbides

Sulfur has been thoroughly shown to be very detrimental to the stress-rupture life of nickel-base alloys at concentrations above approximately 50 ppm. Sulfur strongly segregates to grain boundaries and particularly strongly to carbide-matrix interfaces (Ref 31). The latter segregation affords an opportunity for the formation of sulfocarbides ($M_2SC$), which have been observed in the interdendritic regions of cast alloys in both plate and hexagonal forms (Ref 2).

The $M_2SC$ has a hexagonal crystal structure closely related, with small lattice mismatch, to the fcc structure of MC carbides, but in the $M_2SC$ phase every second layer of carbon is replaced by a layer of sulfur. The flakelike particles have been found to initiate cracks at very small plastic strains in wrought alloys, and it is likely that they act similarly in castings. Although these particles are considered detrimental, sulfur in this form is preferable to sulfur left in interstitial solution at grain boundaries (Ref 2).

## 4.8 Topologically Close-Packed Phases

Topologically close-packed phases are undesirable, and considerable effort is made to avoid compositional ranges that will cause their precipitation during heat treatment or service. In these phases, the atoms are close-packed in layers that are separated by intervening layers of relatively large atoms. They often form as platelike or needlelike precipitates. The tcp phases observed in superalloys include $\sigma\text{-A}_x\text{B}_y$, $\mu\text{-A}_x\text{B}_y$, and Laves-$\text{A}_2\text{B}$ phases, where A is iron, nickel, or cobalt, and B is niobium, molybdenum, tantalum, or chromium. The formation of these phases reduces rupture strength and ductility (Ref 6, 7, 14). It has been observed that the crystal structure of $\text{M}_{23}\text{C}_6$ carbides is very similar to that of the $\sigma$ tcp phase, and the $\text{M}_6\text{C}$ to that of the $\mu$ tcp phase, in alloys that contain molybdenum and tungsten (Ref 7).

The most detrimental tcp phase is the $\sigma$ phase, which has hexagonal symmetry and a composition of $(\text{Cr}_{46}\text{Fe}_{54})$ or $(\text{Ni})_8(\text{Cr,Mo})_4(\text{Cr,Mo,Ni})_{18}$. It is characterized by brittleness and a tendency to form plates or needles, which act as crack initiation and propagation sites (Ref 14, 32). The embrittlement effect is particularly strong at low temperatures and high strain rates. The hard tcp precipitates act as barriers to dislocation motion, which lead to dislocation pile-ups at the precipitate interface, causing loss of cohesion at the interface and crack initiation. This effect is exacerbated by the preferential location of the tcp phases along the grain boundaries. The $\sigma$ phase also contains a high percentage of refractory metal, which depletes the matrix of such solid-solution-hardening elements as molybdenum, tungsten, and rhenium, reducing $\gamma$-matrix strength. In alloys with high $\gamma'$ volume fractions, the $\sigma$ phase can precipitate at the grain boundaries, where the concentration of molybdenum and chromium is high (Fig. 4.11),

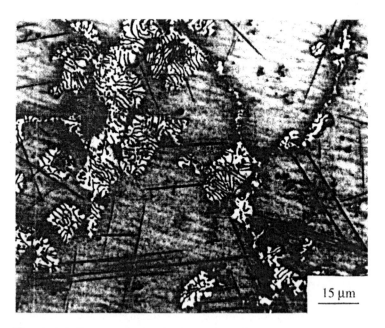

15 µm

**Fig. 4.11** Electron micrograph of experimental Ni-20.7Cr-17Co-0.63Mo-4.75Ti-10Al (at.%) treated at 1180 °C (2160 °F)/4 h/air cooled + 900 °C (1650 °F)/64 h/air cooled showing $\sigma$ plates within the grains and cellular $\sigma/\gamma'$ colonies at the grain boundaries. Source: Ref 14

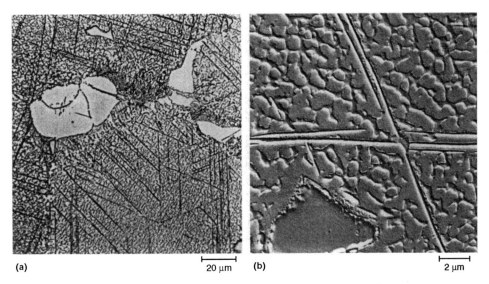

(a)                                      20 μm    (b)                                      2 μm

**Fig. 4.12**  IN-100 nickel-base alloy casting, held at 815 °C (1500 °F) for 5000 h. (a) Structure consists
of massive MC particles, platelets of σ phase, and primary and precipitated γ′ in the γ matrix. (b) Replica-electron micrograph shows a massive particle of MC, Widmanstätten platelets of σ phase,
and γ′ in the γ matrix. Source: Ref 9

or in the dendrite cores, where the concentration of tungsten is high. Commonly, the σ phase precipitates in the Widmanstätten morphology shown
in Fig. 4.12.

To form tcp phases, specific compositions and relatively large amounts
of chromium, molybdenum, and tungsten are necessary (Ref 14). Thus, to
avoid the potentially detrimental consequences of these phases, overall
contents of chromium, molybdenum, and tungsten must be controlled.

Techniques have been developed to determine the susceptibility of any
particular alloy to tcp-phase formation. In particular, the electron vacancy
method ($N_v$), embodied in PHACOMP (Ref 33), has been used to predict
σ-, μ-, and Laves-phase formation in superalloys (Ref 14, 34 to 36). The
method is based on the correlation between tcp-phase formation and the
number of electron vacancies in the γ matrix.

Nickel-iron-base alloys have a greater tendency to form tcp phases because the electronic structure of iron has four vacant d sites, and this structure is more likely to form intermetallics with extremely low interatomic
distances, for example, the Laves and σ phases (Ref 7). This increased
propensity for tcp formation lowers the maximum amount of solid-
solution element that can be tolerated in the iron-containing γ matrix and
therefore restricts the solid-solution strengthening effect; this restriction is
the main drawback to the use of iron in superalloys. The electron configuration of cobalt ($3s^2 3p^6 3d^7 4s^2$) gives the cobalt-base matrix an intermediate tendency for tcp-phase formation, between that of iron ($3s^2 3p^6 3d^6 4s^2$)
and nickel ($3s^2 3p^6 3d^8 4s^2$).

## 4.9 Microstructural Modifications through Heat Treatment

Heat treatment is an important method for modifying the morphology of the precipitates in superalloys. Heat treatment has three primary purposes in superalloys:

- To homogenize the alloy (homogenization heat treatment)
- To dissolve the precipitate in precipitation-hardened alloys (solution heat treatment)
- To precipitate secondary phases in a controlled fashion (aging or precipitation heat treatment)

Other functions of heat treatment include stress relieving, grain growth, and surface modifications (e.g., nitriding, aluminizing). The heat treatments typically used on a variety of superalloys are given in Table 4.3. As can be seen from this table, heat treatment can range from very simple schemes for solid-solution-hardened alloys (alloy 625), through more complex procedures for precipitation-hardened alloys (alloy 718), to the most complex procedures for advanced single-crystal alloys (CMSX-10).

One goal of homogenization heat treatment is the reduction of compositional gradients. In this process, the alloy is heated to an elevated temperature to increase solid-state diffusion and achieve a more uniform distribution of elements; segregation in cast superalloys can be quite remarkable and can lead to the formation of tcp phases. In wrought solid-

**Table 4.3 Approximate solvus temperature of $\gamma'$ for selected superalloys**

| Alloy | Base | Form | $\gamma'$ solvus °C | °F |
|---|---|---|---|---|
| A-286 | Ni-Fe | Wrought | 855 | 1570 |
| Incoloy 901 | Ni-Fe | Wrought | 940 | 1720 |
| Astroloy LC | Ni | Wrought | 1120 | 2050 |
| B-1900 | Ni | Cast | 1150 | 2100 |
| C263 | Ni | Cast | 925 | 1700 |
| CMSX-4 | Ni | Cast | 1305 | 2380 |
| CMSX-10 | Ni | Cast | 1345 | 2450 |
| Inconel 100 | Ni | Cast | 1180 | 2150 |
| Inconel 713LC | Ni | Cast | 1180–1200 | 2150–2190 |
| Inconel 738LC | Ni | Cast | 1160–1175 | 2120–2150 |
| Inconel 792 | Ni | Cast | 1100–1150 | 2010–2100 |
| M-252 | Ni | Wrought | 1010 | 1850 |
| MAR-M 200 | Ni | Cast | 1180–1200 | 2160–2190 |
| MM-006 | Ni | Cast | 1180–1200 | 2160–2190 |
| Nimonic 80A | Ni | Wrought | 960–980 | 1760–1800 |
| Nimonic 90 | Ni | Wrought | 980–1000 | 1800–1830 |
| René 41 | Ni | Wrought | 1050–1070 | 1920–1960 |
| René 95 | Ni | Wrought | 1120–1160 | 2050–2120 |
| René 80 | Ni | Cast | 1150 | 2100 |
| UC01 | Ni | Wrought | 1170 | 2140 |
| Udimet 500 | Ni | Wrought | 1050–1100 | 1920–2010 |
| Udimet 700 | Ni | Cast | 1140 | 2080 |
| Udimet 700 | Ni | Wrought | 1130–1150 | 2070–2100 |
| Waspaloy | Ni | Wrought | 1025–1040 | 1880–1900 |

Source: Ref 1, 15–17

solution-hardened alloys, this processing step is called annealing, and although it still reduces compositional gradients, its main goal is to produce complete recrystallization to achieve maximum softness for forging or other shaping processes.

For precipitation-hardened alloys, solution heat treatment is performed to dissolve (either partially or completely) precipitates formed during casting or aging for the purpose of the controlled reforming of the precipitates in a precipitation hardening treatment (Ref 13). Solution heat treatments are commonly carried out in the temperature range of 1040 to 1230 °C (1900 to 2250 °F), the absolute upper limit being just below the solidus temperature (incipient melting temperature). The objective of a solution heat treatment is merely to dissolve the strengthening precipitate for the purpose of subsequent precipitation hardening, whereas the objective of a homogenization heat treatment is the complete dissolution of all phases and the elimination of as much microsegregation as possible.

In aging, or precipitation hardening, the elements taken into solid solution during solution treatment are precipitated in a favorable type and morphology. This controlled precipitation process is usually a multistep process that takes place at various temperatures. The $\gamma'$ and $\gamma''$ phases are precipitated in this way; secondary carbides can also form in the temperature ranges of 730 to 1040 °C (1350 to 1900 °F) (Ref 36). Carbide formation provides strengthening through coherent precipitates and also delays $\sigma$-phase formation by consuming significant portions of such $\sigma$-forming elements as chromium and molybdenum.

Overaging can produce undesirable precipitate phases and morphologies and should therefore be avoided. For example, overaging of A-286 at 650 °C (1200 °F) results in $\gamma' \rightarrow \eta$ transformation (Ref 1), and overaging of alloy 718 results in $\gamma'' \rightarrow \delta$ transformation (Ref 38).

## 4.10 Rafting

Microstructural changes occur in superalloys during service at elevated temperature; rafting is one such change. Because it occurs over time at elevated temperatures under applied stress, rafted structures are seldom seen in as-manufactured components (Ref 1).

During rafting, the initially discrete $\gamma'$ particles coarsen, forming continuous $\gamma'$ lamellae, or rafts, as shown in Fig. 4.2(f). The lamellae are perpendicular to the direction of an applied tensile stress for a negative lattice mismatch between the matrix and the precipitate, which is the case for the typical superalloy matrix and $\gamma'$ precipitate, and parallel to the direction of an applied stress for a positive lattice mismatch. The situation is reversed for an applied compressive stress. The raft patterns can thus be used to determine the stress state in a failed component (Ref 39).

Rafts can improve the creep resistance of an alloy by providing effective barriers to dislocation motion, effectively forcing a dislocation to shear a γ′ lamella in order to propagate in the perpendicular direction (Ref 12, 39). For example, raft growth has been exploited to produce enhanced creep resistance in a fifth-generation single-crystal alloy (TMS-162) (Ref 40). In general, though, rafting is detrimental to mechanical properties due to the coarseness of the resulting microstructure. Because the shape of the γ′ precipitate is dependent on the lattice mismatch δ, it has been found that δ is one of the driving forces of the rafting process, with faster rafting occurring at higher mismatch values (Ref 12).

## 4.11 Directionally Solidified Superalloys

In polycrystalline superalloys, diffusion and creep deformation occur preferentially at grain boundaries. These are followed by void formation and eventually by cracking. Furthermore, thermal fatigue cracks have been observed to initiate from grain boundaries (Ref 41). Such damage is usually located at grain boundaries and perpendicular to the direction of principal stress.

To prevent such damage, one approach in superalloy development has been the reduction and/or complete removal of grain boundaries. This approach has resulted in the development of directionally solidified (DS) superalloys. There are two main types: columnar-grained (CG) and single-crystal superalloys. The DS superalloys have vastly superior creep resistance compared to polycrystalline alloys, as shown in Table 4.4

In the manufacture of DS alloys, dendrite growth is promoted in a specific direction through the use of a thermal gradient (which can be pro-

### Table 4.4 Common superalloy heat treatments

| Alloy | Alloy type | Solutioning(a) | Aging(a) |
|---|---|---|---|
| A-286 | Wrought, Ni-Fe | 980 °C/1 h/OQ | 720 °C/16 h/AC |
| Discaloy | Wrought, Ni-Fe | 1010 °C/2 h/OQ | 730 °C /20 h/AC + 650 °C/20 h/AC |
| N-155 | Wrought, Ni-Fe | 1175 °C/1 h/WQ | 815 °C/4 h/AC |
| Astroloy | Wrought, Ni | 1175 °C/4 h/AC + 1080 °C/4 h/AC | 845 °C/24 h/AC + 760 °C/16 h/AC |
| Inconel 901 | Wrought, Ni | 1095 °C/2 h/WQ | 790 °C/2 h/AC + 720 °C/24 h/AC |
| Inconel 625 | Wrought, Ni | 1150 °C/2 h/RQ | ... |
| Inconel 713 | Cast, Ni | Used in as-cast condition | ... |
| Inconel 718 | Wrought, Ni | 980 °C/1 h/AC | 720 °C/8 h/FC + 620 °C/8 h/FC |
| Inconel 718 | Cast, Ni | 1095 °C/1 h/AC | 955 °C/1 h/AC + 720 °C/8 h/FC + 620 °C/8 h/AC |
| Inconel 738 | Cast, Ni | 1120 °C/2 h/AC | 845 °C/24 h/AC |
| Nimonic 80A | Wrought, Ni | 1080 °C/8 h/AC | 705 °C/16 h/AC |
| Waspaloy | Wrought/cast, Ni | 1080 °C/4 h/AC | 845 °C/24 h/AC + 760 °C/16 h/AC |
| Haynes 25 | Wrought, Co | 1230 °C/1 h/RAC | ... |
| Haynes 188 | Wrought, Co | 1230 °C/0.5 h/RAC | ... |
| S-816 | Wrought, Co | 1175 °C/1 h/RQ | 760 °C/12 h/AC |
| CMSX-2 | Cast, Ni (single crystal) | 1315 °C/3 h/GFQ | 980 °C/5 h/AC + 870 °C/20 h/AC |
| PWA-1480 | | 1290 °C/4 h/GFQ | 1080 °C/4 h/AC + 870 °C/32 h/AC |
| CMSX-10 | Cast, Ni (single crystal) | 1316 °C/1 h + 1329 °C/2 h + 1327 °C/2 h + 1340 °C/2 h + 1346 °C/2 h + 1352 °C/3 h, 1357 °C/3 h + 1360 °C/5 h + 1363 °C/10 h + 1365 °C/15 h | 1152 °C/6 h/AC + 871 °C/24 h/AC + 760 °C/30 h/AC |

(a) AC = air cool, FC = furnace cool, GFQ = gas furnace quench, OQ = oil quench, RAC = rapid air cool, RQ = rapid quench to below 540 °C, WQ = water quench. Source: Ref 1, 37

vided by a chill plate and gradual mold withdrawal), producing a microstructure in which all of the grains are oriented in the same direction. The grain growth direction is deliberately chosen to correspond to the direction in which cubic crystal dendrites grow preferentially, namely the <100> direction. Fortunately, this is typically also the direction of greatest resistance to creep and thermal fatigue because of the low elastic modulus (Ref 6), although anisotropy is a function of alloy composition. Achieving such preferred <100> crystal growth is difficult even under stringently controlled manufacturing conditions, particularly for large turbine blades; slight deviations of up to 10° from the ideal are typically allowed in practice (Ref 14). Local misorientation defects in the microstructure are called high- or low-angle grain boundaries, according to whether they are greater or less than 15°.

The very first commercial CG alloys were developed by VerSnyder at Pratt and Whitney (Ref 5, 34, 35), in which the entire component was composed of columnar grains, and the longitudinal axis was aligned with the direction of highest applied stress (which is normal to the rotational axis for axial turbine blade components). A notable CG superalloy is MAR-M 200 (Table 4.5), which, for a while, was the leading CG superalloy, but its low grain-boundary ductility led to the modification of the alloy through hafnium additions in the 1970s, resulting in PWA 1422.

Single-crystal superalloys were the next step in development. The manufacturing process is similar to that used for CG alloys, except that a "pigtail" constriction is added to eliminate all but the single fastest-growing grain, which usually has the <100> orientation. Single-crystal superalloys can be grouped by development stage into first-, second-, and third-generation alloys, with certain compositions characterizing each development stage (Table 4.6).

The first generation of single-crystal superalloys is represented by such alloys as PWA 1480, CMSX-2, René N4, SRR 99, AM1, and MC2, which are essentially CG alloys with slightly modified compositions. The introduction of rhenium at approximately three weight percent into the alloying system characterizes the second generation, represented by such alloys as CMSX-4, PWA 1484, and René N5. The third generation contains more rhenium (five to six weight percent) and less chromium to prevent the formation of the σ phase; it is represented by such alloys as CMSX-10 and René N6. Because of its increased refractory content, this generation can

**Table 4.5 Creep properties of MAR-M 200 with different grain structures**

| Grain structure(a) | 1400 °F/100 ksi (760 °C/700 MPa) | | | 1600 °F/50 ksi (870 °C/350 MPa) | | | 1800 °F/30 ksi (980 °C/200 MPa) | | |
|---|---|---|---|---|---|---|---|---|---|
| | Rupture life, h | Elongation, % | Minimum creep rate (× 10−5/h) | Rupture life, h | Elongation, % | Minimum creep rate (× 10−5/h) | Rupture life, h | Elongation, % | Minimum creep rate (× 10−5/h) |
| PC | 4.9 | 0.45 | 70 | 245.9 | 2.2 | 3.4 | 35.6 | 2.6 | 23.8 |
| CG | 366.0 | 12.6 | 14.5 | 280.0 | 35.8 | 7.7 | 67.0 | 23.6 | 25.6 |
| SX | 1914.0 | 14.5 | 2.2 | 848.0 | 18.1 | 1.4 | 107.0 | 23.6 | 16.1 |

(a) PC, polycrystalline; CG, columnar grained; SX, single crystal. Source: Ref 1

**Table 4.6 Chemical compositions of selected single-crystal alloys**

| Alloy | Chemical composition(a), wt% | | | | | | | | | | | |
|---|---|---|---|---|---|---|---|---|---|---|---|---|
| | Cr | Co | Mo | W | Ta | V | Nb | Al | Ti | Hf | Re | Ru |
| **1st generation** | | | | | | | | | | | | |
| PWA 1480 | 10 | 5 | ... | 4 | 12 | ... | ... | 5 | 1.5 | ... | ... | ... |
| PWA 1483 | 12.8 | 9 | 1.9 | 3.8 | 4 | ... | ... | 3.6 | 4 | ... | ... | ... |
| René N4 | 9 | 8 | 2 | 6 | 4 | | 0.5 | 3.7 | 4.2 | ... | ... | ... |
| SRR 99 | 8 | 5 | ... | 10 | 3 | ... | ... | 5.5 | 2.2 | ... | ... | ... |
| RR 2000 | 10 | 15 | 3 | ... | ... | 1 | ... | 0.05 | 4 | ... | ... | ... |
| AM1 | 8 | 6 | 2 | 6 | 9 | ... | ... | 0.05 | 1.2 | ... | ... | ... |
| AM3 | 8 | 6 | 2 | 5 | 4 | ... | ... | 5.2 | 2 | ... | ... | ... |
| CMSX-2 | 8 | 5 | 0.6 | 8 | 6 | ... | ... | 6 | 1 | ... | ... | ... |
| CMSX-3 | 8 | 5 | 0.6 | 8 | 6 | ... | ... | 5.6 | 1 | 0.1 | ... | ... |
| CMSX-6 | 10 | 5 | 3 | ... | 2 | ... | ... | 4.8 | 4.7 | 0.1 | ... | ... |
| CMSX-11B | 12.5 | 7 | 0.5 | 5 | 5 | ... | 0.1 | 3.6 | 4.2 | 0.1 | ... | ... |
| CMSX-11C | 14.9 | 3 | 0.4 | 4.5 | 5 | ... | 0.1 | 3.4 | 4.2 | 0.04 | ... | ... |
| SX792 | 12 | 8 | 2 | 4 | 5 | ... | ... | 3.4 | 4.2 | 0.04 | ... | ... |
| AF56 | 12 | 8 | 2 | 4 | 5 | ... | ... | 3.4 | 4.2 | ... | ... | ... |
| SC16 | 16 | ... | 3 | ... | 3.5 | ... | ... | 3.5 | 3.5 | ... | ... | ... |
| **2nd generation** | | | | | | | | | | | | |
| CMSX-4 | 7 | 9 | 0.6 | 6 | 7 | ... | ... | 5.6 | 1 | 0.1 | 3 | ... |
| PWA 1484 | 5 | 10 | 2 | 6 | 9 | ... | ... | 5.6 | 0 | 0.1 | 3 | ... |
| SC 180 | 5 | 10 | 2 | 5 | 9 | ... | ... | 5.2 | 1 | 0.1 | 3 | ... |
| MC2 | 8 | 5 | 2 | 8 | 6 | ... | ... | 5 | 1.5 | ... | ... | ... |
| René N5 | 7 | 8 | 2 | 5 | 7 | ... | ... | 6.2 | ... | 0.2 | 3 | ... |
| **3rd generation** | | | | | | | | | | | | |
| CMSX-10 | 2 | 3 | 0.4 | 5 | 8 | ... | ... | 5.7 | 0.2 | 0.03 | 6 | ... |
| René N6 | 4.2 | 12.5 | 1.4 | 6 | 7.2 | ... | 0.1 | 5.75 | ... | 0.15 | 5.4 | ... |
| TMS 75 | 3 | 12 | 2 | 6 | 6 | ... | ... | 6 | ... | 0.1 | 5 | ... |
| TMS 113 | 2.89 | 11.93 | 1.99 | 5.96 | 5.96 | ... | ... | 6.56 | ... | 0.1 | 5.96 | ... |
| **4th generation** | | | | | | | | | | | | |
| TMS 138 | 3.0 | 6.0 | 3.0 | 3.0 | 6.0 | ... | ... | 6.0 | ... | 0.1 | 5.0 | 2.0 |
| **5th generation** | | | | | | | | | | | | |
| TMS 162 | 3.0 | 6.0 | 4.0 | 6.0 | 6.0 | ... | ... | 6.0 | ... | 0.1 | 5.0 | 6.0 |

(a) bal Ni. Source: Ref 39, 40, 42

withstand temperatures up to 1200 °C (2200 °F). They do have higher density than their predecessors and therefore add weight to engines, but the fact that they can operate up to 85 percent of their absolute melting temperature (Ref 14) compensates for the additional weight through increased efficiency and reduced fuel consumption.

The most recent research, leading toward the fourth and fifth generations of single-crystal superalloys, uses ruthenium. Ruthenium suppresses dendritic segregation, promotes a more uniform distribution of alloying elements between dendrite cores and interdendritic regions, and retards the formation of tcp phases (Ref 43, 44).

The increased creep resistance of DS superalloys extends their useful service temperature. The replacement of polycrystalline IN-738C vanes in a Rolls Royce turbofan engine by single-crystal CM-186LC permits an increase in turbine temperature of more than 93 °C (200 °F) (Ref 45), which translates into significantly higher engine efficiency. This improvement in alloy temperature properties is summarized in Table 4.7.

**Table 4.7 Temperature ranges for superalloys in turbine blade applications**

| Superalloy type | Maximum useful temperature | | Incipient melting point | |
|---|---|---|---|---|
| | °C | °F | °C | °F |
| Conventional cast | 1121 | 2050 | 1204–1232 | 2200–2250 |
| Columnar grain | 1121 | 2050 | 1204–1232 | 2200–2250 |
| Single crystal | 1232 | 2250 | 1277–1316 | 2330–2400 |
| Oxide dispersion strengthened | 1343 | 2450 | 1399 | 2550 |

Source: Ref 1

**Fig. 4.13** Transmission electron micrograph of the microstructure of γ' in a dendrite in (left) as-cast CMSX-10 and (right) after standard heat treatment. Source: Ref 37

The significant phases observed in single-crystal superalloys are γ' (Fig. 4.13), MC carbides, and tcp phases. The γ' assumes a cuboidal morphology, and MC carbides tend to form in the interdendritic regions during final solidification. The γ dendrite core regions, as shown in Fig. 4.14, are enriched in such elements as rhenium, molybdenum, chromium, cobalt, and tungsten and have lower levels of aluminum, titanium, hafnium, niobium, and tantalum than the interdendritic regions (Ref 14). The tendency of molybdenum, rhenium, and chromium to segregate to the dendrite core region rises dramatically for increasing rhenium concentration (Ref 46). The segregation of tantalum toward the interdendritic regions increases with the addition of melting-point depressants, for example, boron, carbon, and hafnium, and as a result, carbide formation increases as well. In the immediate vicinity of MC carbides, enrichment by chromium, rhenium, cobalt, and molybdenum occurs, and MC-carbide-forming elements tantalum, niobium, and titanium are depleted.

The tendency of an element to segregate in an alloy is quantified by its chemical partitioning coefficient, $k'$, which is defined as the ratio of the dendrite core concentration to the interdendritic concentration. The $k'$ values are determined experimentally and are simply an expression of the average degree of segregation to be expected for each element in each alloy. In an experiment where 4% Ru was added to an experimental alloy,

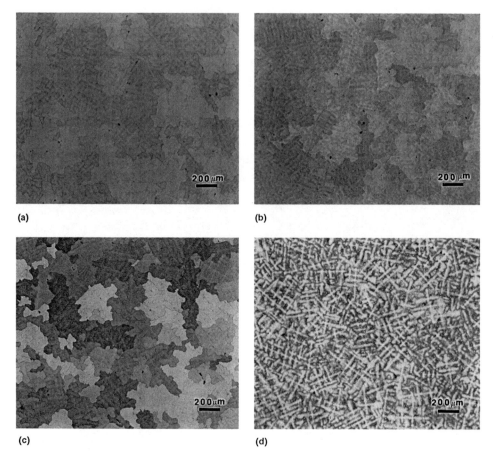

(a)

(b)

(c)

(d)

**Fig. 4.14** Cast dendritic structure of IN-738 nickel-base alloy. The varying features of the microstructure are revealed by using different etchants. Source: Ref 9

the segregation, as measured by $k'$, of rhenium, chromium, and molybdenum was reduced by approximately 63, 50, and 63 percent, respectively. The ruthenium addition reduced the overall segregation of the alloy to less than that of an otherwise equivalent rhenium-free alloy, thus effectively regaining the full benefits of the rhenium addition without the associated adverse segregation effect (Ref 46).

Because there are steep compositional gradients between the dendrite cores and the interdendritic regions of single-crystal superalloys, the dendrite cores tend to be rich in tcp-forming elements, and tcp phases therefore tend to form. Although some degree of homogenization does occur during solution heat treatment, long heat treatment times are required because of the low diffusion rates of tcp-forming elements such as molybdenum, tungsten, and rhenium.

The formation of a σ phase initiates in the dendrite core regions, because the composition is rich in the elements that form this phase (rhenium, chromium, molybdenum, tungsten, cobalt, and nickel). The σ phase forms as thin plates upon high-temperature exposure, with their longitudinal growth restricted by the nucleation of other σ plates. In single-crystal superalloys containing grain-boundary strengtheners (hafnium, boron, carbon), σ-phase formation can also initiate in the interdendritic regions near MC carbides, as shown in Fig. 4.15, because these regions are also rich in the σ-phase-forming elements due to the microsegregating effect of the carbides (Ref 47). The formation of a σ phase in the vicinity of MC carbides is further assisted by the fact that the carbides and σ phase have similar crystal structures and are highly coherent, but the growth of these σ plates is restricted by the MC carbide and dependent on the availability of σ-forming elements in the region surrounding the carbide (Ref 24). The conditions that favor σ-phase precipitation (chromium, molybdenum, and cobalt enrichment) can also favor the precipitation of $M_{23}C_6$ carbides. Because the carbide has a lower free energy than the σ phase, the presence of carbon in the dendritic region can promote the formation of $M_{23}C_6$, retarding σ-phase formation by depleting chromium, molybdenum, and cobalt (although not rhenium). The consumption of tantalum, niobium, and titanium by MC carbide formation has also been observed to reduce σ-phase formation. The consumption of these γ'-forming elements through carbide formation reduces the γ' volume fraction, improving microstructural stability but reducing strength (Ref 47).

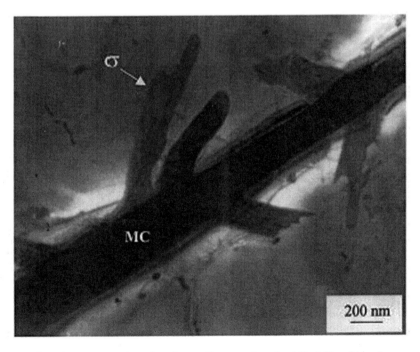

**Fig. 4.15** Formation of σ plates adjacent to interdendritic MC carbides in SX-RR2072 during exposure at 950 °C (1740 °F). Source: Ref 48

The detrimental μ phase also tends to form in the dendritic cores as a consequence of the local composition (Ref 32). It is generally believed that μ-phase precipitation is detrimental to creep resistance; however, in one study involving alloys MC2 and AM3, the μ phase has been shown to have little or no effect on the creep resistance of the alloys up to μ-phase concentrations as high as approximately 0.85 volume percent. In MC2, the μ phase forms at elevated temperatures and can be clearly observed to introduce local disturbances in the regularity of the γ/γ′ rafted microstructure (Fig. 4.16); in AM3, no μ-phase precipitation occurs under similar conditions (Fig. 4.17). Thus, by using these two alloys, the study was able to separate the effects of rafting from those of the μ-phase precipitate. The same study also considered the impact of the μ phase on low-cycle fatigue, tensile strength, and impact strength, concluding that the presence of the μ phase is inconsequential at concentrations below approximately 0.15 volume percent and affects the creep response only when the volume fraction is above the aforementioned level of 0.85 percent. Rafting and γ′ coarsening were found to have greater influence than the precipitation of the μ phase on the degradation of mechanical properties at high temperatures (Ref 32).

The μ phase precipitates from the γ matrix, similarly to σ-phase precipitation, depleting the adjacent regions of tungsten, molybdenum, and chromium and thereby softening the γ matrix. This elemental depletion induces the γ→ γ′ transformation, leading to a microstructure in which the μ-phase particles are enveloped by the γ′ phase. The formation of significant amounts of μ phase requires relatively high concentrations of the strength-

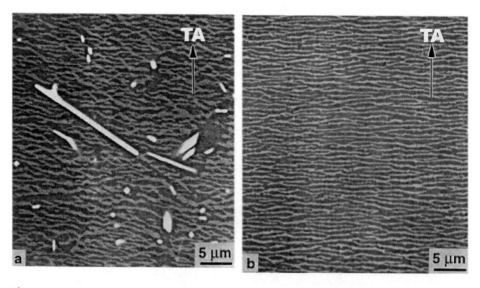

**Fig. 4.16** Scanning electron micrographs of the longitudinal section of (a) MC2 and (b) AM3 stress-aged alloys (200 h, 1050 °C/80 MPa, or 1920 °F/12 ksi). M-phase precipitates appear white in backscattered electron mode. TA: tensile axis. Source: Ref 32

**Fig. 4.17** Scanning electron micrograph of µ-phase precipitates electrochemically extracted from an overaged MC2 single-crystal sample. The γ/γ' matrix observed in the background is only partially dissolved. Source: Ref 32

ening elements that induce it, a fact that may explain why there is a threshold below which the presence of the µ phase appears to not have a significant effect (Ref 32).

The yield of the single-crystal casting process is quite low, particularly for large airfoils, and therefore, the cost of single-crystal components is high. Another factor contributing to the increased cost of single-crystal superalloy manufacturing is the homogenization heat treatment. The homogenization heat treatment process can be quite long, and it is prone to produce rejectable defects such as recrystallization (Ref 45).

It is possible to counterbalance these factors to a degree by reintroducing grain-boundary strengtheners such as boron, carbon, and zirconium, as in CM-186LC and CMSX-486. These elements can increase the misorientation tolerance of the alloy and stabilize the defect regions. As a result, higher yields can be achieved in both casting and homogenization by relaxing production tolerances while maintaining properties within design parameters.

## REFERENCES

1. M.J. Donachie and S.J. Donachie, *Superalloys: A Technical Guide,* 2nd ed., ASM International, 2002
2. R.T. Holt and W. Wallace, Impurities and Trace Elements in Nickel-Base Superalloys, *Int. Met. Rev.,* Vol 21, 1976, p 1–14
3. E.F. Bradley, Ed., *Superalloys: A Technical Guide,* ASM International, 1988
4. L. Liu, T. Huang, et al., Grain Refinement of Superalloy K4169 by Addition of Refiners: Cast Structure and Refinement Mechanisms, *Mater. Sci. Eng. A,* Vol 394, 2005, p 1
5. C.T. Sims, Superalloys: Genesis and Character, *Superalloys II,* C.T. Sims, N.S. Stoloff, and W.C. Hagel, Ed., John Wiley & Sons, 1987, p 3–26
6. P. Kumar, The Role of Niobium and Tantalum in Superalloys, *Advances in High Temperature Structural Materials and Protective Coatings,* A.K. Koul, Ed., National Research Council of Canada, Ottawa, 1994, p 34–53
7. E.W. Ross and C.T. Sims, Nickel-Base Alloys, *Superalloys II,* C.T. Sims, N.S. Stoloff, and W.C. Hagel, Ed., John Wiley & Sons, 1987, p 97–133
8. N.S. Stoloff, Fundamentals of Strengthening, *Superalloys II,* C.T. Sims, N.S. Stoloff, and W.C. Hagel, Ed., John Wiley & Sons, 1987, p 61–96
9. *Metallography and Microstructures,* Vol 9, *ASM Handbook,* ASM International, 2004
10. W.T. Loomis, J.W. Freeman, and D.L. Sponseller, The Influence of Molybdenum on the $\gamma'$ Phase in Experimental Nickel-Base Superalloys, *Metall. Trans.,* Vol 3, 1972, p 989–1000
11. T. Maebashi and M. Doi, Coarsening Behaviors of Coherent Gamma Prime and Gamma Precipitates in Elastically Constrained Ni-Al-Ti Alloys, *Mater. Sci. Eng. A,* Vol 373, 2004, p 72–79
12. R.A. McKay, M.V. Nathal, and D.D. Pearson, Influence of Molybdenum on the Creep Properties of Nickel-Base Superalloy Single Crystals, *Metall. Trans. A,* Vol 21 (No. 2), 1990, p 381–388
13. H.S. Ko, K.W. Paik, L.J. Park, Y.G. Kim, and J.H. Tundermann, Influence of Rhenium on the Microstructures and Mechanical Properties of a Mechanically Alloyed Oxide Dispersion-Strengthened Nickel-Base Superalloy, *J. Mater. Sci.,* Vol 33, 1998, p 3361–3370
14. M. Durand-Charre, *The Microstructure of Superalloys,* Gordon and Breach Science Publishers, Amsterdam, 1997, p 1–124
15. G.E. Fuchs and B. Boutwell, Modelling of the Partitioning and Phase Transformation Temperatures of an As-Cast Third Generation Single Crystal Ni-Base Superalloy, *Mater. Sci. Eng. A,* Vol 333 (No. 1–2), 2002, p 72

16. C. Walter, B. Hallstedt, and N. Warnken, Simulation of the Solidification of CMSX-4, *Mater. Sci. Eng. A,* Vol 397, 2005, p 385–390

17. A. Manonukul, F. Dunne, and D. Knowles, Physically-Based Model for Creep in Nickel-Base Superalloy C263 Both Above and Below the Gamma Solvus, *Acta Mater.,* Vol 50, 2002, p 2917–2931

18. J.A. Manriquez, P.L. Bretz, L. Rabenberg, and J.K. Tien, The High Temperature Stability of IN718 Derivative Alloys, *Superalloys 1992,* S.D. Antolovich et al., Ed., TMS, 1992, p 507–516

19. A.M. Beltran, Cobalt-Base Alloys, *Superalloys II,* C.T. Sims, N.S. Stoloff, and W.C. Hagel, Ed., John Wiley & Sons, 1987, p 135–163

20. Y. Murata, K. Suga, and N. Yukawa, Effects of Transition Elements on the Properties of MCrAlY Carbides in IN-100 Nickel-Based Superalloy, *J. Mater. Sci.,* Vol 21 (No. 10), 1986, p 3653–3660

21. J.M. Nell and N.J. Grant, Multiphase Strengthened Nickel Base Superalloys Containing Refractory Carbide Dispersions, *Superalloys 1992,* S.D. Antolovich et al., Ed., TMS, 2002, p 113–121

22. W.H. Jiang, X.D. Yao, H.R. Guan, and Z.Q. Hu, Secondary $M_6C$ Precipitation in a Cobalt-Base Superalloy, *J. Mater. Sci. Lett.,* Vol 18, 1999, p 303–305

23. Microstructure of Wrought Heat-Resisting Alloys, *Atlas of Microstructures of Industrial Alloys,* Vol 7, *Metals Handbook,* 8th ed., American Society for Metals, 1972, p 157–176

24. J.M. Poole, J.J. Fischer, G.A.J. Hack, and G.M. McColvin, The Development, Performance and Future of the Mechanical Alloying Process and Oxide Dispersion Strengthened Alloys, *Advances in High Temperature Structural Materials and Protective Coatings,* A.K. Koul, Ed., National Research Council of Canada, Ottawa, 1994, p 34–53

25. S. Schoonbaert, X. Huang, S. Yandt, and P. Au, Brazing and Wide Gap Repair of X-40 Using Ni-Base Alloys, *J. Gas Turbines Power,* Vol 130 (No. 3), 2008, p 032101

26. M.F. Hupalo, M. Terada, A.M. Kliaugua, and A.F. Padilha, Microstructural Characterization of Incoloy Alloy MA 956, *Mater.wiss. Werkst.tech.,* Vol 34, 2003, p 505–508

27. O.P. Sinha, V. Chatterjee, V. Sarma, and S. Jha, Effect of Residual Elements on High Performance Nickel Base Superalloys for Gas Turbines and Strategies for Manufacture, *Bull. Mater. Sci.,* Vol 28 (No. 4), 2005, p 379–382

28. J. Davis, *Nickel, Cobalt, and Their Alloys, ASM Specialty Handbook,* ASM International, 2000

29. K.L. Dahm, K. Short, and G. Collins, Characterization of Nitrogen-Bearing Surface Layers on Ni-Base Superalloys, *Wear,* Vol 263, 2007, p 625–628

30. V. Singh and M. Efstathios, Synthesis, Characterization and Proper-

ties of Intensified Plasma-Assisted Nitrided Superalloy Inconel 718, *Surf. Coat. Technol.,* Vol 201, 2006, p 1093–1101

31. J.X. Dong, X. Xie, and R. Thompson, The Influence of Sulfur on Stress-Rupture Fracture in INCONEL 718 Superalloys, *Metall. Mater. Trans. A,* Vol 31, 2000, p 2135–2144

32. M. Simonetti and P. Caron, Role and Behavior of Mu Phase during Deformation of a Nickel-Based Single Crystal Superalloy, *Mater. Sci. Eng. A,* Vol 254, 1998, p 1–12

33. H. Murphy, C. Sims, and A. Beltran, PHACOMP Revisited, *Superalloys 1968,* M. Donachie, Ed., TMS, 1968, p 47–66; e-book: www .tms.org

34. B. J. Piearcy and F. L. Versnyder, A New Development in Gas Turbine Materials: The Properties and Characteristics of PWA 664, *J. Aircr.,* Vol 3 (No. 5), 1966, p 390

35. *Properties and Selection: Nonferrous Alloys and Pure Metals,* Vol 2, *Metals Handbook,* 9th ed., American Society for Metals, 1979, p 1–155

36. J.R. Mihalisin and D.L. Pasquine, Phase Transformations in Nickel-Base Superalloys, *Superalloys 1968,* TMS, 1968, p 134–170

37. C. Schulze and M. Feller-Kniepmeier, Transmission Electron Microscopy of Phase Composition and Lattice Misfit in the Re-Containing Nickel-Base Superalloy CMSX-10, *Mater. Sci. Eng. A,* Vol 281, 2000, p 204–212

38. T. Shibata, Y. Shudo, and Y. Yoshino, Effects of Aluminum, Titanium and Niobium on the Time-Temperature Precipitation Behavior of Alloy 706, *Superalloys 1996,* R.D. Kissinger et al., Ed., TMS, 1996, p 153–162

39. M. Kamaraj, Rafting in Single Crystal Nickel-Base Superalloys—An Overview, *Sadhana,* Vol 28 (Parts 1 and 2), 2003, p 115–128

40. J.X. Zhang, Y. Koizumi, et al., Strengthening by $\gamma/\gamma'$ Interfacial Dislocation Networks in TMS-162—Toward a Fifth Generation Single Crystal Superalloy, *Metall. Mater. Trans. A,* Vol 35, 2004, p 1911–1914

41. R.J. Quigg, Tantalum's Effect on Nickel-Base Superalloys, *Proc. International Symposium on Tantalum and Niobium,* Nov 1988, p 619–629

42. G.L. Erikson, in *Superalloys,* R.D. Kissinger **et al.,** Ed., TMS-AIME, 1996, p 35

43. R. Kearsey, "Compositional Effects of Microsegregation Behaviour in Single Crystal Superalloy Systems," Ph.D. thesis, Carleton University, 2004

44. I.G. Wright and T. B. Gibbons, Recent Developments in Gas Turbine Materials and Technology and Their Implications for Syngas Firing, *Int. J. Hydrogen Energy,* Vol 32, 2007, p 3610–3621

45. J.B. Wahl, K. Harris, and T.L. Moore, Grain Boundary Strengthened Single Crystal Superalloys, *Proc. Advanced Materials and Processes for Gas Turbines,* Sept 22–26, 2002, p 129–135

46. R. Kearsey, J. Beddoes, K. Jaansalu, W. Thompson, and P. Au, "The Effects of Re, W, and Ru on Microsegregation Behaviour in Single Crystal Superalloy Systems," Superalloys 2004

47. Q.Z. Chen and D.M. Knowles, Retardation of Sigma-Phase Transformation in Modified Superalloy RR2072, *Metall. Mater. Trans. A,* Vol 33 (No. 5), 2002, p 1319–1330

48. Q.Z. Chen, N. Jones, and D.M. Knowles, The Macrostructures of Base/Modified RR2072 SX Superalloys and Their Effects on Creep Properties at Elevated Temperatures, *Acta Mater.,* Vol 50, 2002, p 1095–1112

CHAPTER **5**

# Compositional Effects

THE PRIMARY GOAL in superalloy development is to obtain an alloy with optimal mechanical properties at high temperatures while providing sufficient environmental resistance, although component designers have become increasingly dependent on coatings and cooling systems to make up for any shortcoming in environmental resistance. The study of alloying elements in superalloys is extremely broad, covering most of the periodic table, as shown in Fig. 5.1.

Elemental additions in superalloys are chosen to modify mechanical properties, surface stability, or cost. Such properties as yield strength,

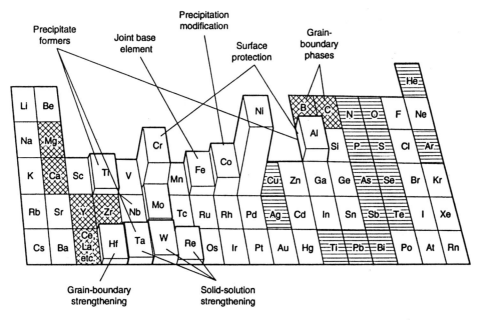

**Fig. 5.1** Alloying elements in nickel-base superalloys. Beneficial minor elements are indicated by cross-hatching, while detrimental tramp elements are marked with horizontal lines. Source: Ref 1

toughness, ductility, low-cycle fatigue life, and creep life can be adjusted through modifications of composition and various microstructural features, such as $\gamma/\gamma'$ lattice mismatch, $\gamma'$ volume fraction, diffusion rates, antiphase-boundary energy, and stacking fault energy. Surface stability improvement is achieved through the formation of a protective surface oxide scale composed largely of chromium and/or aluminum oxides. Reactive elements yttrium, cerium, hafnium, and lanthanum have also been used to improve the adherence of the protective oxide scale to the substrate.

This chapter discusses the typical compositional ranges of superalloys, the major base metals used in such alloys (iron, cobalt, and nickel), and the effects of the most common alloying elements (chromium, aluminum, and titanium). It also discusses the effects of refractory elements, grain-boundary elements, reactive elements, oxides, and trace elements.

## 5.1 Typical Compositional Ranges

The type and amount of alloying elements in superalloys are strongly dependent on the intended application and the life-cycle cost, which determine the superalloy family and principal strengthening mechanisms. In general, cobalt-base alloys have the highest chromium contents due to their preferred use in applications susceptible to hot corrosion and the requirement to form $M_{23}C_6$ and $M_6C$ carbides for strengthening, because cobalt alloys are not precipitation hardenable. Chromium can also provide some solid-solution hardening in cobalt-base alloys. The refractory elements in all superalloy families provide solid-solution hardening to the $\gamma$ matrix. Aluminum is added to form strengthening precipitates in nickel- and nickel-iron-base superalloys and to impart oxidation resistance through the formation of an alumina scale. Iron is used when possible, simply to reduce cost. Titanium also forms strengthening precipitates in nickel-base alloys and, to a small degree, in cobalt-base superalloys. Nickel is an essential alloying addition in cobalt- and nickel-iron-base superalloys and is used to stabilize the face-centered cubic (fcc) matrix within the service temperature range. Niobium is added for $\gamma''$ precipitate formation and also for solid-solution hardening. Tantalum is added for carbide formation and solid-solution hardening. Tantalum also has the peculiarity of segregating to the interdendritic liquid preferentially over the dendrites, which tends to reduce freckling (see section 5.6.4, "Tantalum," in this chapter). Rhenium is added mainly for solid-solution hardening in single-crystal alloys and has a significant positive influence on the creep life. Ruthenium has been added to the new generation of single-crystal alloys to suppress dendritic segregation and inhibit topologically close-packed phase (tcp) formation. Lastly, carbon is added for carbide formation, which strengthens grain boundaries significantly. Carbon level can also influence the workability of the alloy.

The range of these alloying additions is given in Table 5.1, which summarizes alloy percentage range as well as the average content (enclosed in parentheses). The function of each of these elements is dependent both on the nature of the element (atomic mass, size, electron configuration) and on the alloy to which it is added. The elemental additions used for specific purposes in various alloys are given in Table 5.2, the individual effects for each element are tabulated in Table 5.3, and the characteristic properties of each element are included in Appendix B.

**Table 5.1    Compositional ranges (wt%) of major alloying additions in superalloys**

Average content is indicated in parentheses.

| Element | Nickel-iron base Wrought | Cobalt base Wrought | Cobalt base Cast | Nickel base Wrought | Nickel base Cast |
|---|---|---|---|---|---|
| Cr | 0–22 (14) | 18–30 (22) | 3–30 (22) | 1–28 (17) | 0–30 (10) |
| Al, Ti | 0–5.5 (2) | 0–3.5 (0.8) | 0–4.3 (0.1) | 0–10 (3) | 0–10.5 (6.5) |
| Mo, W, Re, Ru | 0–9.6 (2) | 0–15 (6) | 0–27 (9) | 0–28 (5.5) | 0–22 (7.5) |
| Nb, Ta | 0–5 (1.5) | 0–7.5 (1.7) | 0–9 (2.1) | 0–6.5 (0.8) | 0–12 (2.5) |
| Fe | 16–67 (43) | 0–21 (5) | 0–4 (1) | 0–38 (6) | 0–18 (0.6) |
| Co | 0–34 (6.5) | 22–64 (43) | 36–68 (58) | 0–29 (7) | 0–22 (8.8) |
| Ni | 0–49 (30) | 0–43 (18) | 0–28 (10) | 37–80 (57) | 48–75 (60) |
| C | 0–0.4 (0.1) | 0.05–1.0 (0.2) | 0.1–1.0 (0.4) | 0.01–0.4 (0.08) | 0.003–0.5 (0.1) |
| B, Zr | 0–0.1 (0.006) | 0–1.5 (0.2) | 0–2.0 (0.2) | 0–0.15 (0.02) | 0–1.5 (0.08) |
| Hf | Not common | Not common | Not common | 0–0.35 (0.1) | 0–1.8 (0.3) |

**Table 5.2    Elements required for selected alloying effects in superalloys**

| Effect | Nickel-iron base | Cobalt base | Nickel base |
|---|---|---|---|
| Solid-solution strengtheners | Cr, Mo | Nb, Cr, Mo, Ni, W, Ta | Co, Cr, Fe, Mo, W, Ta, Re, Al, Ti |
| Face-centered cubic matrix stabilizer | C, W, Ni | Ni, Fe | … |
| Carbide formation: | | | |
|   MC | Ti, Nb, Ta | Ti, Nb, Ta | W, Ta, Ti, Mo, Nb, Hf |
|   $M_7C_3$ | … | Cr | Cr |
|   $M_{23}C_6$ | Cr | Cr | Cr, Mo, W |
|   $M_6C$ | Mo | Mo, W, Nb, Ta | Mo, W, Nb, Ta |
| Carbonitride (MCN) precipitation | C, N | C, N | C, N |
| Promotes carbide precipitation | P | … | … |
| $\gamma'$ Ni$_3$(Al,Ti) precipitation | Al, Ni, Ti | … | Al, Ti |
| Retards formation of hexagonal η (Ni$_3$Ti) | Al, Zr | … | … |
| Raises solvus temperature of $\gamma'$ | Co | … | Co |
| Hardening precipitates and/or intermetallics | Al, Ti, Nb, Ta | Al, Mo, Ti, W, Ta | Al, Ti, Nb, Ta |
| Oxidation resistance | Cr | Al, Cr | Al, Cr, Y, La, Ce |
| Improves hot corrosion resistance | La, Y | La, Y, Th | La, Th |
| Sulfidation resistance | Cr | Cr | Cr, Co, Si |
| Improves creep properties | B | … | B, Ta, Re |
| Increases rupture strength | B | B, Zr | B |
| Grain-boundary refiners | B, C | B, C, Zr | B, C, Zr, Hf |
| Facilitates working | B, C | Fe, Ni$_3$Ti, B, C | Fe, B, C |
| Retards $\gamma'$ coarsening | … | … | Re |

Source: Ref 1, 2

**Table 5.3   Effects of notable alloying elements in superalloys**

| Element | Nickel-iron base | Cobalt base | Nickel base |
|---|---|---|---|
| Cr | • Improves hot corrosion and oxidation resistance<br>• Solid-solution hardening | • $M_{23}C_6$ and $M_7C_3$ carbide precipitation<br>• Improves hot corrosion and oxidation resistance<br>• Promotes topologically close-packed (tcp) phases | • Improves hot corrosion and oxidation resistance<br>• $M_{23}C_6$ and $M_7C_3$ carbide precipitation<br>• Moderate solid-solution hardening<br>• Moderate increase in $\gamma'$ volume fraction<br>• Promotes tcp phases |
| Al | • $\gamma'$ precipitation<br>• Retards formation of hexagonal $\eta$ $Ni_3Ti$ | • Improves oxidation resistance<br>• Forms intermetallic $\beta$-CoAl | • Moderate solid-solution hardening<br>• $\gamma'$ precipitation<br>• Improves oxidation resistance |
| Ti | • $\gamma'$ precipitation<br>• TiC carbide precipitation | • TiC carbide precipitation<br>• Formation of $Co_3Ti$ intermetallic<br>• Formation of $Ni_3Ti$ with sufficient Ni<br>• Reduces surface stability | • Moderate solid-solution hardening<br>• $\gamma'$ precipitation<br>• TiC carbide precipitation |
| Mo | • Solid-solution hardening<br>• $M_6C$ carbide precipitation | • Solid-solution hardening<br>• Formation of $Co_3Mo$ intermetallic<br>• Promotes tcp phases | • High solid-solution hardening<br>• Moderate increase in $\gamma'$ volume fraction<br>• $M_6C$ and MC carbide formation<br>• Increases density<br>• Promotes tcp phases ($\sigma$, $\mu$) |
| W | • Solid-solution hardening<br>• $M_6C$ carbide precipitation | • Solid-solution hardening<br>• Formation of $Co_3W$ intermetallic<br>• Promotes tcp phases | • High solid-solution hardening<br>• Moderate increase in $\gamma'$ volume fraction<br>• $M_6C$ carbide formation<br>• Increases density<br>• Promotes tcp phases ($\sigma$, $\mu$) |
| Ta | • $\gamma''$ precipitation<br>• TaC carbide precipitation | • MC and $M_6C$ carbide precipitation<br>• Formation of $Co_2Ta$ intermetallic<br>• Reduces surface stability | • High solid-solution hardening<br>• TaC carbide precipitation<br>• Large increase in $\gamma'$ volume fraction<br>• Improves oxidation resistance |
| Nb | • $\gamma''$ precipitation<br>• NbC carbide precipitation<br>• $\delta$-$Ni_3Nb$ precipitation | • MC and $M_6C$ carbide precipitation<br>• Formation of $Co_2Nb$ intermetallic<br>• Reduces surface stability | • High solid-solution hardening<br>• Large increase in $\gamma'$ volume fraction<br>• NbC carbide formation<br>• Promotes $\gamma'$ formation<br>• $\gamma''$ precipitation<br>• $\delta$-$Ni_3Nb$ precipitation |
| Re | ... | ... | • Moderate solid-solution hardening<br>• Retards coarsening<br>• Increases $\gamma/\gamma'$ lattice mismatch |
| Fe | Not applicable | • Improves workability | • Decreases oxidation resistance<br>• Promotes tcp phases ($\sigma$, Laves)<br>• Improves workability |
| Co | ... | Not applicable | • Raises $\gamma$ solidus temperature<br>• Moderate increase in $\gamma'$ volume fraction (some alloys)<br>• Raises $\gamma'$ solvus temperature |
| Ni | • Face-centered cubic (fcc) matrix stabilizer<br>• Inhibits tcp-phase precipitation | • fcc stabilizer<br>• Decreases hot corrosion resistance | • Not applicable |
| C | • Forms MC, $M_7C_3$, $M_6C$, and $M_{23}C_6$ carbides<br>• Stabilizes fcc matrix | • Carbide formation<br>• Decreases ductility | • Carbide formation<br>• Moderate solid-solution hardening |
| B | • Improves creep strength and ductility<br>• Retards formation of grain-boundary $\eta$ $Ni_3Ti$ | • Improves creep strength and ductility | • Moderate solid-solution hardening<br>• Inhibits carbide coarsening<br>• Improves grain-boundary strength<br>• Improves creep strength and ductility |
| Zr | • Improves creep strength and ductility<br>• Retards formation of grain-boundary $\eta$ $Ni_3Ti$ | • MC carbide formation<br>• Improves creep strength and ductility<br>• Reduces surface stability | • Moderate solid-solution hardening<br>• Inhibits carbide coarsening<br>• Improves grain-boundary strength<br>• Improves creep strength and ductility |
| Hf | ... | ... | • Improves creep strength and ductility<br>• Improves grain-boundary strength<br>• HfC formation<br>• Promotes eutectic $\gamma/\gamma'$ formation |

Source: Ref 1, 3, 4

## 5.2 Base Elements

The base element in a superalloy is a key in determining its properties, and the three base elements in common use are iron, cobalt, and nickel. Their various advantages and disadvantages make individual alloys suitable for different applications. A brief summary is given in Table 5.4.

The choice of iron, cobalt, or nickel as the base metal has significant implications for overall performance, but these three elements are not just used as base metals. All three are used as alloying additions in other super-alloy systems.

### 5.2.1 Iron

Because iron has inherently poor properties, no iron-base superalloys exist (with the exception of ferritic MA-956). Instead, nickel is added to the iron matrix to form nickel-iron-base superalloys. Adding iron to nickel- and cobalt-base alloys improves workability, but the main reason for using iron in superalloys is its lower cost in comparison to nickel or cobalt. However, iron has a tendency to form tcp phases due to the four vacant d sites in iron favoring the formation of intermetallics with short interatomic distances. Another problem with adding iron to nickel is that the $\gamma'$ and $\gamma''$ phases in nickel-iron-base superalloys are metastable and transform to $\eta$ and $\delta$, respectively, over time at elevated temperature.

### 5.2.2 Cobalt

The cobalt-base matrix has intermediate properties between those of nickel-iron and nickel, including the tendency to form tcp phases (see section 4.8, "Topologically Close-Packed Phases," in Chapter 4 of this book). Of the three base elements, cobalt has the highest melting temperature and

**Table 5.4  Principal effects of superalloy base elements on alloy characteristics**

| Base element | Advantages | Disadvantages | Typical applications |
|---|---|---|---|
| Fe | • Low cost<br>• Increases workability | • Low environmental resistance<br>• Low strength at high temperatures<br>• Requires face-centered cubic (fcc) stabilizer<br>• Higher propensity for topologically close-packed (tcp)-phase precipitation | • Suitable for high toughness, low-temperature applications<br>• Disks, turbine casings |
| Co | • Highest incipient melting point (unalloyed metal)<br>• High corrosion resistance | • No strengthening precipitate comparable to $\gamma'$ or $\gamma''$<br>• Requires fcc stabilizer<br>• Cobalt prices have been known to be volatile in the past. | • Suitable for creep-resistant applications with low stresses or where hot corrosion resistance is required<br>• Industrial gas turbine engines (GTEs), vanes |
| Ni | • Forms strengthening $\gamma'$ and $\gamma''$ precipitates<br>• Requires no fcc stabilizer<br>• Lower propensity for tcp-phase formation | • Reduced environmental resistance compared to cobalt<br>• High cost | • Highest strength and creep resistance at high temperatures<br>• GTE blades, vanes, disks |

Source: Ref 3, 5–7

therefore performs better than the others at high temperatures with relatively low alloying levels in applications for which very high strength is not needed. That is why it is used in turbine vanes and other low-load-bearing components.

The main disadvantage of cobalt in commercial superalloys is that it is no longer available at low cost. Cobalt was a major additive in nickel-base superalloys (for example, Nimonic 90, Waspaloy, and Udimet 500, 700, 710, and 720) until the 1970s, with cobalt contents typically in the 15 to 20 wt% range. However, in the late 1970s, cobalt prices rose drastically; half of the world's cobalt reserves are located in central Africa (Democratic Republic of Congo and Zimbabwe), which leads to an issue of reliability of supply. Consequently, the price has risen to unsustainable levels (Ref 8). Lack of access to a reliable and economical supply of cobalt has tended to reduce the use of both cobalt-base superalloys and cobalt as an additive in other superalloy systems. Another disadvantage of cobalt is that it forms no effective strengthening precipitates comparable to $\gamma'$ in nickel-iron- and nickel-base superalloys.

The rise in cobalt prices during the 1970s prompted further examination of the effects of cobalt additions on nickel-iron- and nickel-base superalloys—examination that produced a number of contradictory views. Some researchers found that the role of cobalt is minor as an elemental addition. A study, corroborated by four manufacturers (Ref 9), on cobalt-reduced Waspaloy (from 13.5 to 7.75 wt% Co) indicated that reduction of cobalt levels in the alloy had no effect on yield or tensile strengths and only a minor effect on stress-rupture life, an effect that could be countered by refining the grain size. It was also found that the same amount of $\gamma'$ phase could be produced even with reduced cobalt by increasing the levels of aluminum and titanium. Other researchers found that cobalt levels did have an effect on stress-rupture life (Ref 1), as shown in Fig. 5.2, and that this effect was especially strong in alloys designed for disk applications. The only common conclusion is that the effect of the cobalt level on the stress-rupture properties of an alloy is strongly related to its aluminum/titanium ratio and that the effect is greatest when this ratio is less than 1.0.

Cobalt increases the creep life of single-crystal nickel-base superalloys at intermediate temperatures of 700 to 850 °C (1290 to 1560 °F), but cobalt-containing single-crystal superalloys are highly sensitive to the orientation of the crystal with respect to the applied tensile load (Ref 10). Cobalt-free single-crystal nickel-base superalloys are less sensitive to crystallographic orientation and therefore more suited to the complex loads borne by such components as air-cooled turbine blades. The effect of cobalt on creep resistance is prevalent at intermediate temperatures, where rafting does not readily occur. At temperatures where rafting does occur, cobalt additions provide insignificant enhancements of creep resistance compared to that provided by rafting.

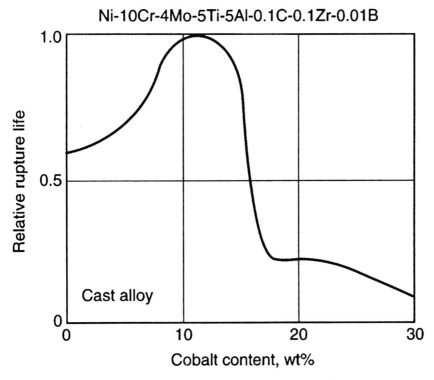

**Fig. 5.2** Rupture strength at 1020 °C (1870 °F) of a nickel-base superalloy as a function of cobalt content. Source: Ref 1

Although cobalt is known to modify $\gamma'$ coarsening and volume fraction, the operative mechanisms are not clear. Generally, addition of cobalt is believed to counteract overaging and precipitate dissolution (Ref 2) and increase the $\gamma'$ volume fraction (Ref 1, 5). One study concludes that cobalt increases the high-temperature, above 1100 °C (2010 °F), solubility of aluminum + titanium in the $\gamma$ matrix and permits a higher volume fraction of $\gamma'$ to precipitate during aging (Ref 1); another concludes that cobalt reduces the low-temperature solubility of aluminum + titanium, also resulting in a higher $\gamma'$ volume fraction upon aging (Ref 5). The increase in high-temperature solubility of aluminum plus titanium not only improves the $\gamma'$ volume fraction but also facilitates hot working of the alloy. It has been found that cobalt substitutes for nickel in $\gamma'$ precipitates (Ref 5, 11).

Cobalt has very limited influence on solid-solution hardening of the nickel matrix, because the two atoms have similar atomic radii. Cobalt can raise the solidus temperature in the nickel-cobalt binary system, as shown in Table 5.5, although this effect is minor when compared to the levels that can be achieved through rhenium, ruthenium, iridium, or tungsten (also shown in Table 5.5) additions.

**Table 5.5  Effect of 1 wt% alloying element on melting points ($\Delta T_M$ °C) of nickel and cobalt**

|  | Al | B | C | Cr | Co | Fe | Mn | Mo | Ni | Nb | Si | S | Ta | Ti | W | V | Zr |
|---|---|---|---|---|---|---|---|---|---|---|---|---|---|---|---|---|---|
| Ni ($T_M$ = 1454 °C) | −6 | >−278 | −250 | −2.8 | +0.6 | −1.1 | −10 | −3.9 | ... | −8.9 | −33 | >−556 | −2.8 | −14 | +1.7 | −2.8 | >−56 |
| Co ($T_M$ = 1495 °C) | −11 | >−278 | >−167 | −2.8 | ... | −0.6 | −8.3 | −4.4 | −0.6 | −39 | −42 | >−556 | −17 | −36 | +0.6 | −8.3 | −17 |

Source: Ref 12

### 5.2.3 Nickel

Nickel has a low propensity for tcp-phase formation because its third electron shell is nearly filled. It provides good solubility for secondary elements that can strengthen it directly through solid-solution hardening or indirectly through precipitate formation. Nickel-base superalloys are the workhorse materials in the most demanding environments of a gas turbine engine.

For cobalt- and nickel-iron-base superalloys, nickel is used mainly as an fcc matrix stabilizer. Additions of up to 20 weight percent Ni (or Fe) are used to suppress the fcc → hexagonally close-packed (hcp) transformation in cobalt-base superalloys (Ref 3), whereas at least 25 weight percent Ni is necessary to suppress the fcc→ body-centered cubic (bcc) transformation in nickel-iron-base superalloys (Ref 7). An increase in the nickel content decreases the carbon solubility, which leads to greater carbide precipitation for a given carbon content (Ref 2). A beneficial effect of nickel is observed in wrought cobalt-base alloys, where it lowers deformation resistance and improves workability. However, in these alloys, the nickel additions are kept below 10 weight percent to avoid decreases in rupture strength. The addition of nickel to nickel-iron-base alloys permits the formation of strengthening γ′ and γ″ precipitates.

## 5.3 Chromium

Chromium is present in almost all superalloys and strongly affects both environmental resistance and mechanical properties. With respect to environmental resistance, the primary effect of chromium is that it permits a reduction in the aluminum content of the alloy by aiding the formation of surface alumina at lower aluminum concentrations (Ref 13, 14), effectively modifying the aluminum activity in the alloy (Ref 15). The presence of as little as 5 to 10 weight percent Cr reduces the amount of aluminum required to form a protective alumina scale from 40 to approximately 10 atomic percent (Ref 16). Chromium also assists in the formation of a chromia ($Cr_2O_3$) scale that forms a buffer against basic fluxing of nickel, iron, and cobalt oxides during hot corrosion attack (Ref 16, 17). This scale is particularly advantageous because, as compared to alumina scale, it forms faster and provides better protection from hot corrosion. The improvement in hot corrosion resistance due to chromium can be clearly seen in

Table 5.6. Approximately 25 to 40 weight percent Cr is required for good type II hot corrosion at 670 to 750 °C (1240 to 1380 °F) protection; 15 to 20 weight percent Cr is required for good type I hot corrosion at 800 to 950 °C (1470 to 1740 °F) protection (Ref 16). Chromium levels of 25 weight percent can be found in superalloys; these are usually found in the environmental-resistance-optimized superalloys, because high chromium levels are incompatible with desirable mechanical properties due to tcp-phase formation.

As an example of the increased environmental resistance provided by chromium, alloy 690 (Ni-30Cr-10Fe) is replacing alloy 600 (Ni-16Cr-9Fe) as the material for steam generator tubes in pressurized water nuclear reactors due to its superior resistance to intergranular stress-corrosion cracking (IGSCC) (Ref 18). Alloy 690 tends to form only $Cr_{23}C_6$ carbides in the grain boundaries, whereas alloy 600 forms both $Cr_7C_3$ and $Cr_{23}C_6$ carbides. The precipitation of carbides in the grain boundaries causes localized chromium depletion, which reduces the IGSCC resistance in acidic environments but has a negligible effect in high-purity water.

Chromium and aluminum levels must be evaluated together to determine what type of protective oxide scale is predominant. If the chromium-to-aluminum ratio is greater than four, the alloy is considered a chromia former. If the ratio is less than four, the alloy is considered an alumina former (Ref 19). The main type of oxide scale of a few selected superalloys is listed in Table 5.7.

With respect to mechanical properties, the most important role of chromium is in the gradual formation at high temperatures of secondary $M_{23}C_6$ and $M_6C$ carbides from the primary MC and $M_6C$ carbides. Secondary carbides are the primary strengthening phases in cobalt-base superalloys, and they provide additional strengthening in nickel- and nickel-iron-base

**Table 5.6  Effect of chromium content on the hot corrosion resistance of nickel- and cobalt-base superalloys as measured with a burner rig test with 5 ppm of sea salt injection**

| Alloy | Chromium content, % | Loss in sample diameter, mm | | | |
|---|---|---|---|---|---|
| | | 870 °C (1600 °F), 500 h | 950 °C (1740 °F), 1000 h | 980 °C (1800 °F), 1000 h | 1040 °C (1900 °F), 1000 h |
| MAR-M 200 | 9.0 | 1.6 | 3.3+ | ... | ... |
| IN-100 | 10.0 | 3.3+ | 3.3+ | ... | ... |
| SEL-15 | 11.0 | 3.3+ | 3.3+ | ... | ... |
| Alloy 713 | 13.0 | 3.3+ | 2.0+ | ... | ... |
| Udimet 700 | 14.8 | 1.7+ | 1.6 | ... | ... |
| SEL | 15.0 | 1.2 | 1.3 | 0.3 | ... |
| Udimet 500 | 18.5 | 0.2 | 0.8 | 0.7 | ... |
| René 41 | 19.0 | 0.3 | ... | 0.8 | ... |
| Hastelloy X | 22.0 | ... | 0.3 | 0.4 | ... |
| L605 (alloy 25) | 20.0 | ... | 0.4 | 0.3 | 1.1 |
| WI-52 | 21.0 | 0.5 | 0.5 | ... | 1.9 |
| MAR-M 509 | 21.5 | ... | 0.3 | ... | 0.8 |
| MAR-M 302 | 21.5 | 0.14 | 0.3 | ... | 0.6 |
| X-40 | 25.0 | 0.11 | 0.3 | ... | 0.5 |

Source: Ref 1

Table 5.7    Main oxide constituent of protective oxide scale for selected superalloys

| Chromia formers | | | Alumina formers | | |
|---|---|---|---|---|---|
| Superalloy | Chromium, wt% | Aluminum, wt% | Superalloy | Chromium, wt% | Aluminum, wt% |
| Nimonic 80A | 19.5 | 1.4 | B-1900 | 8 | 6 |
| X-40 | 22 | 0 | IN-100 | 10 | 5.5 |
| S-816 | 20 | 0 | Alloy 713C | 12.5 | 6 |
| Waspaloy | 19.5 | 3 | MAR-M 200 | 9 | 5 |
| Udimet 500 | 19 | 3 | Udimet 700 | 15 | 4.3 |

Source: Ref 20

superalloys. Chromium is the main element in the secondary $M_{23}C_6$ carbide, which often causes the precipitation of this phase in alloys with a chromium content of 10 to 15 weight percent and almost always in alloys containing 18 to 20 weight percent Cr (Ref 12).

Chromium can also substitute for both nickel and aluminum in $\gamma'$; in this respect, its behavior is similar to that of molybdenum and iron (Ref 5). The coarsening rate of $\gamma'$ in Ni-Cr-Ti-Al alloys decreases with increasing chromium content in the 10 to 37 weight percent range because of a reduction in the equilibrium concentration of $\gamma'$ in $\gamma$ and a reduction in coherency strains (Ref 5). This can be discerned from the Ni-Cr-Al phase diagram (Ref 4), which illustrates reduced $\gamma'$ fraction with increased chromium content (Ref 21). The reduced $\gamma'$ fraction compromises strength, particularly at high temperatures, and is another significant drawback to high chromium levels (Ref 1). As discussed in section 2.1.1, "Precipitation-Hardened Nickel-Iron Alloys," in Chapter 2 of this book, chromium levels are kept minimal in the low-thermal-expansion alloys because of the Curie temperature-reduction effect caused by chromium.

The chromium content in superalloys has been reduced incrementally over the years of superalloy evolution because of the propensity of chromium to form tcp phases. High levels of chromium can also lead to hot tearing (the formation of cracks in a casting during the final stages of solidification) during the casting of columnar-grained alloys (Ref 22). For alloys with low chromium content, surface coatings are often applied to improve corrosion resistance.

## 5.4 Aluminum

Like chromium, aluminum is present in most nickel- and nickel-iron-base superalloy families and is a significant factor in enhancing both mechanical properties and environmental resistance, but excessive aluminum addition degrades ductility. Upon exposure to the atmosphere, the aluminum in the alloy forms a tenacious, protective $Al_2O_3$ scale that protects the alloy from further oxidation by impeding the inward diffusion of oxygen. However, alumina-forming alloys are less resistant to $Na_2SO_4$-induced oxidation than chromia-forming alloys. Aluminum is also used in the form of aluminized coatings or MCrAlY coatings, mainly for use at temperatures greater than 900 °C (1650 °F), to enhance oxidation resistance.

In addition to its major role in providing alloy oxidation resistance, aluminum also plays a significant role in the strengthening mechanisms of nickel- and nickel-iron-base superalloys. In these alloys, aluminum is added to form $\gamma'$ precipitate, although elements such as titanium, niobium, and tantalum can substitute for aluminum in $\gamma'$ formation (Ref 5). Aluminum partitions preferentially to the $\gamma'$ phase, with a $\gamma/\gamma'$ partitioning ratio of one to four (Ref 23), although this is highly dependent on overall alloy nominal composition. High aluminum contents have also been observed to delay the detrimental $\gamma' \rightarrow \eta$ transformation in nickel-iron-base alloys (Ref 5).

One of the main difficulties in the precipitation hardening of nickel-iron-base superalloys is that the strengthening $\gamma'$ phase is stable only within a narrow range of aluminum/titanium ratios, as typified by the modified stainless steel described in Fig. 5.3. In this alloy, because of the relatively large titanium/aluminum ratio required, $\gamma'$ precipitation is possible only for relatively low aluminum levels, limiting the volume fraction of $\gamma'$ that can precipitate and therefore the maximum strength the alloy can achieve (Ref 4). However, although low aluminum levels are necessary for $\gamma'$ formation in nickel-iron-base superalloys, higher aluminum levels can be

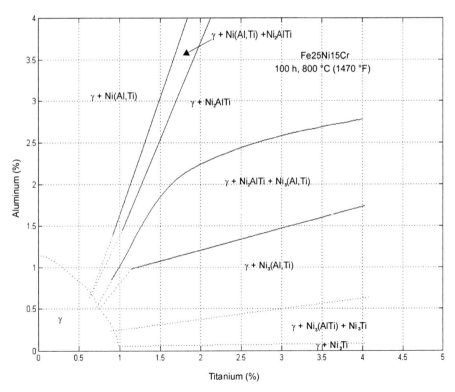

**Fig. 5.3** Effect of aluminum and titanium contents on the phases present at 800 °C (1470 °F) in Fe-15Cr-25Ni-modified stainless steel. Source: Ref 4

used to promote strengthening through $\gamma''$ precipitation. In most nickel-iron-base superalloys, the aluminum content is balanced to promote the co-precipitation of $\gamma'$ and $\gamma''$, which gives the alloys higher strength over a wider temperature range (Ref 24).

Through its influence on the volume fraction of $\gamma'$ phase, aluminum also has an indirect but major influence on the weldability of superalloys (Ref 4, 25). Whereas solid-solution-hardened alloys can generally be fusion-welded successfully, precipitation-hardened alloys are prone to strain age cracking (postweld heat treatment cracking as the rapid formation of $\gamma'$ causes a loss of ductility) and heat-affected zone (HAZ) liquation cracking (cracks due to partial melting and material segregation in the HAZ). In $\gamma''$ alloys, the postweld precipitation in the HAZ occurs much more slowly, allowing thermal stresses in the weldment to be more readily accommodated without cracking. As shown in Fig. 5.4, weldability decreases with increasing $\gamma'$ volume fraction, which can be correlated to aluminum + titanium contents; the weldability line in Fig. 5.4 is described approximately as two times aluminum concentration (wt%) + titanium concentration (wt%) < 6.0.

## 5.5 Titanium

Titanium encourages the formation of $\gamma'$ precipitates and is more effective than aluminum in raising the solvus temperature and lattice parameter of the $\gamma'$ phase (Ref 27). Titanium provides additional strengthening by increasing the antiphase-boundary energy for $\gamma'$ (Ref 28). Titanium tends to partition to the $\gamma'$ phase, thereby drastically reducing the solubility of chromium and molybdenum in this phase (Ref 27). This may have detrimental effects on alloy properties, because it will effectively enrich the $\gamma$ matrix with tcp-phase-forming elements. Titanium also modifies the properties of the $\gamma''$ phase. In nickel-iron-base superalloys, such as alloy 706, it is observed that even if aluminum and niobium are present in large amounts, the $\gamma''$ phase will not precipitate in the absence of titanium (Ref 24). Titanium is also a strong MC-type carbide former.

Titanium additions in wrought cobalt-base alloys, for example, CM-7 and Jetalloy 1650, have produced a coherent, ordered-fcc $(Co,Ni)_3Ti$ precipitate, analogous to $\gamma'$. This precipitate provides strength up to the phase stability limits of approximately 760 °C (1400 °F). However, titanium content greater than five weight percent can produce detrimental hcp-$Co_3Ti$ and/or $Co_2Ti$ Laves phases (Ref 3).

Titanium additions contribute to hot tearing during manufacturing, a significant issue in directionally solidified alloys. Control over the titanium/tantalum ratio, two elements that partition preferentially to the interdendritic liquid, can have noticeable effects on the hot tearing behavior of columnar-grained Inconel 792 (Ref 29). Specifically, poor castability is observed when the titanium/tantalum ratio is between 0.7 and 1.0. Tita-

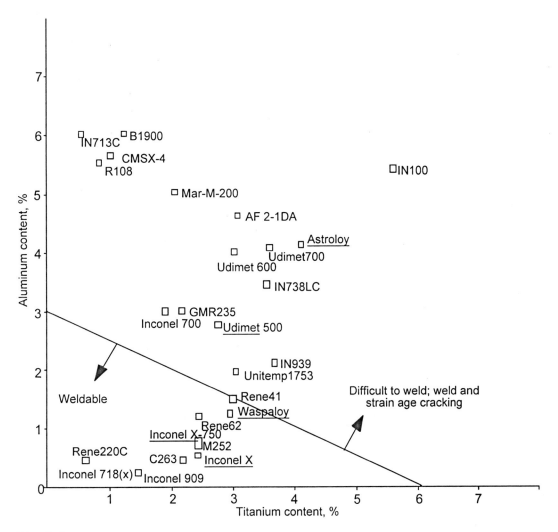

**Fig. 5.4** Weldability assessment diagram for superalloys. Source: Ref 26

nium increases the hot workability of conventional polycrystalline Ni-Cr-W alloys (Ref 30); the maximum improvement is achieved at 0.08 weight percent Ti. Titanium can be used to control nitrogen levels in superalloy melts. The bonding with nitrogen reduces voids, but the brittle TiN reduces machinability (Ref 12).

Using titanium as an alloying element has major drawbacks in cost, because titanium is a relatively expensive element compared to other alloying additions. Moreover, because of the high reactivity of titanium, the only way to process high-titanium alloys is by vacuum casting, which also adds to manufacturing costs. In general, it was the development of vacuum casting technology that permitted the high levels of reactive aluminum and titanium to be added to modern nickel-base superalloys.

# 5.6 Refractory Elements

Modern superalloys depend on extensive use of the refractory elements molybdenum, tungsten, niobium, tantalum, and rhenium for solid-solution hardening of the $\gamma$ phase (Ref 20). The most effective solid-solution hardeners are molybdenum and tungsten, followed by niobium and tantalum (Ref 4). These elements may also form carbides and detrimental tcp phases if overall compositions are not designed adequately. Although hafnium is a refractory element, its role is more akin to that of boron, carbon, and zirconium, and its effects are covered in section 5.7.4, "Hafnium," in this chapter. The use of refractory elements is limited in practice by tcp-phase formation and density increase, the latter being a major issue affecting inertial loads in all rotating components (or, more specifically, the strength-to-density ratio is the major issue) and weight in aeronautical gas turbines.

Molybdenum and tungsten are also carbide formers. They form $M_6C$ carbides in alloys with high levels of refractory alloying elements (for example, B-1900, MAR-M 200, MAR-M 246, René 41) and mixed $M_{23}C_6$ and $M_6C$ carbides in alloys with lower refractory levels. Molybdenum and tungsten are also capable of forming MC carbides, but they bond more weakly with carbon than titanium and niobium do; as a result, WC and MoC can degrade to the more stable forms $M_{23}C_6$ and $M_6C$ after heat treatment or service (Ref 5). Doping IN-100 with low levels (approximately 0.81 atomic percent) of tungsten and tantalum causes a more homogeneous MC carbide distribution (Ref 31). Although not directly a strengthening effect, certain refractory element additions, namely rhenium and tungsten (and also the nonrefractory elements ruthenium and iridium), can increase the solidus and liquidus temperature of the nickel matrix (Ref 32).

Molybdenum and tungsten not only influence alloy strength directly but can also modify the behavior of other strengthening elements. For example, the presence of molybdenum and tungsten in Ni-22Cr-2.8Ti-3.1Al reduces the diffusivity of titanium and chromium at 900 °C (1650 °F) (Ref 5), which can influence the stability of both carbide and $\gamma'$. This influence is evidenced by a retarded ripening rate of $\gamma'$ when molybdenum and tungsten are present. Moreover, because molybdenum, tantalum, tungsten, and niobium are believed to increase $\gamma'$ antiphase-boundary energy, these refractory alloying elements can further enhance $\gamma'$ strengthening (Ref 28).

Addition of refractory elements can particularly benefit single-crystal superalloys. Tantalum, niobium, hafnium, and rhenium can increase the $\gamma'$ solvus temperature and the volume fraction of $\gamma'$, resulting in increased strength and creep resistance at higher temperatures. Additions of tantalum, molybdenum, and hafnium result in reduced freckling (chains of equiaxed grains in columnar-grained or single-crystal alloys) in directionally solidified castings, although the presence of hafnium is undesirable because it lowers the incipient melting point of the nickel matrix. Tanta-

**Table 5.8  Optimal rhenium and tungsten levels for creep life in second-generation single-crystal superalloy**

| Test conditions | Optimal rhenium + tungsten content |
|---|---|
| 850 °C/500 MPa (1560 °F/73 ksi) | Replacing 2 parts Re by 1 part W achieves equivalent $t_{1\%}$ life and reduces alloy density 1–2%. |
| 980 °C/230 MPa (1800 °F/33 ksi) | The ratio of Re to W must be kept constant (1.3). Sharp drop in creep resistance at Re < 2.3 wt%. Optimum is 2.3 wt% Re, 3.0 wt% W. |
| 1100 °C/120 MPa (2010 °F/17 ksi) | Time to failure increases with Re + W content. Replacing 2 parts Re by 1 part W achieves equivalent $t_{1\%}$ life and reduces alloy density 1–2%. |

Source: Ref 33, 34

lum and tungsten are more effective than niobium, vanadium, and molybdenum in increasing the strength of γ′, probably by increasing the antiphase-boundary energy of the γ′ phase. Tantalum, tungsten, and rhenium are beneficial in producing fine γ′ precipitates during service, although rhenium is more effective than tantalum and tungsten due to its low solubility in γ′ (Ref 2).

Despite several beneficial effects, it is desirable to keep refractory-element concentrations to a minimum to reduce alloy density, which is particularly important in single-crystal superalloys used for aircraft gas turbine engines. Efforts to reduce combined rhenium and tungsten concentration have resulted in significant decreases in the creep rates of second-generation single-crystal superalloys. The influence of these two elements on creep behavior depends on the temperature regime. The results of a study aimed at determining minimum tungsten and rhenium concentrations for three different temperatures on a proprietary second-generation single-crystal superalloy determined that the optimal rhenium and tungsten concentrations for creep resistance depend on the temperature (Table 5.8) (Ref 33, 34). At 850 °C (1560 °F), the simple substitution of two parts rhenium by one part tungsten did not affect the creep resistance but reduced the alloy density by one to two percent. At 980 °C (1800 °F), at least 2.3 weight percent Re was required for adequate creep resistance, and a tungsten-to-rhenium ratio of 1.3 maximized the creep resistance of the alloy. At 1100 °C (2010 °F), rafting was observed, but the time to failure and time to reach one percent strain were increased by simply increasing the total amount of rhenium + tungsten. The same 2-to-1 substitution effect as observed at the 850 °C (1560 °F) test prevailed (Ref 33, 34).

Refractory elements have a mixed influence on environmental resistance. Molybdenum and tungsten provide aqueous corrosion resistance, with such commercial examples as Hastelloy B-2 (28 weight percent Mo), Hastelloy C-276 (16 weight percent Mo), Hastelloy C-22 (13 weight percent Mo), Inconel 625 (9 weight percent Mo), and Hastelloy G-30 (5 weight percent Mo and 2.5 weight percent W) (Ref 20). However, molybdenum, tungsten, and vanadium also have detrimental effects when the surface of the alloy is attacked by type II hot corrosion (acid fluxing) (Ref 17). The general corrosion attack when molybdenum is present is described by the following reactions:

$$Mo + \tfrac{3}{2} O_2 \rightarrow MoO_3$$
$$MoO_3 + SO_4^{2-} \rightarrow MoO_4^{2-} + SO_3$$
$$Al_2O_3 + 3MoO_3 \rightarrow 2Al^{3+} + 3MoO_4^{2-}$$

This type of hot corrosion reaction has two particularly detrimental features:

- Protective oxides (alumina) may dissolve in the salt melt and reprecipitate as nonprotective constituents.
- The reaction is self-sustaining (Ref 35).

The refractory content in superalloys is limited for the same reasons chromium content is limited: to avoid detrimental σ-phase formation (Ref 36). The function of individual refractory elements is further discussed in the following sections.

### 5.6.1 Molybdenum

The main effect of molybdenum is to increase the strength of the $\gamma$ matrix through solid-solution hardening, due to its large atomic size and preferential partitioning to the $\gamma$ phase. The $\gamma/\gamma'$ partitioning ratio of molybdenum is four to one, although this value can vary depending on overall alloy composition (Table 5.9) (Ref 23).

The partitioning behavior of molybdenum in $\gamma$ can be modified by the presence of other alloying elements. Titanium influences the solubility of molybdenum in the $\gamma'$ phase; molybdenum dissolves extensively in the $\gamma'$ phase of titanium-free alloys and to a lesser extent in the $\gamma'$ phase of alloys with a high titanium/aluminum ratio (Ref 5, 27). It has been reported that in the Ni-Cr-Al-Mo system, at molybdenum concentrations up to one atomic percent, there is a preferential molybdenum partitioning to the $\gamma'$ phase (Ref 27). As the molybdenum content is increased to above one atomic percent, it preferentially partitions to the $\gamma$ matrix. Tantalum, like titanium, reduces the solubility of molybdenum in the $\gamma'$ phase (Ref 23). Increasing concentrations of tungsten also increase the solubility of molybdenum in both the $\gamma$ and $\gamma'$ phases in nickel-base alloys (Ref 28).

Molybdenum has a lower solid-solution strengthening effect than tungsten because of its smaller atomic radius (Ref 28). Molybdenum can also influence strength indirectly, by increasing the lattice parameter of the $\gamma$ phase and thus influencing lattice mismatch between $\gamma$ and $\gamma'$. Its effect on

Table 5.9 $\gamma/\gamma'$ partitioning ratios

| Alloy | Mo | Ta | W | Nb |
|---|---|---|---|---|
| Udimet 710 | 3.33 | ... | 0.8 | ... |
| B-1900 | 5.26 | 2.10 | ... | ... |
| IN-738 | 3.70 | 1.03 | 1.52 | 0.69 |

Source: Ref 28

the $\gamma'$ phase is much smaller than that of other refractories, because molybdenum has less tendency to occupy the aluminum sites in $\gamma'$ than tantalum, niobium, or tungsten.

The effect of molybdenum on superalloy properties is not limited to tensile strength. Like all refractory elements, its large atomic size leads to inherently low diffusivity, which results in improved creep properties for the alloy with higher molybdenum contents (Ref 23). Although tantalum also exhibits this positive influence on creep life, its effect is not as remarkable as that of molybdenum.

A drastic loss of creep life can occur with excess molybdenum additions, as shown in Fig. 5.5 for an experimental single-crystal superalloy, because of the precipitation of an orthorhombic NiMo phase, which disrupts the continuous and uniform $\gamma/\gamma'$ lamellae formed during the rafting process.

Despite a low solubility in $\gamma'$, molybdenum does influence its properties. Molybdenum increases the lattice parameter, solvus temperature (Fig. 5.6), and weight fraction of $\gamma'$. Molybdenum affects $\gamma'$ volume fraction by reducing the solubility of aluminum in the $\gamma$ matrix. Compositionally, molybdenum reduces the chromium content in $\gamma'$ phase significantly (Ref 27).

### 5.6.2 Tungsten

Tungsten is a heavy refractory element with the highest melting point of 3407 °C, (6165 °F) of any metal and a density of 19.3 g/cm$^3$ (0.7 lb/in.$^3$), which is slightly lower than that of rhenium (21.0 g/cm$^3$, or 0.76 lb/in.$^3$). Its atomic radius (0.137 nm) is very close to that of molybdenum (0.136 nm). The low diffusivity of tungsten, which is a consequence of its large mass, reduces the coarsening rates for $\gamma'$ precipitates. The behavior of tungsten is very similar to that of rhenium and molybdenum in that it segregates preferentially to the $\gamma$ phase, where it provides solid-solution hardening because of the large $\gamma/\gamma'$ lattice misfit. Like molybdenum, it also reduces formability. Like rhenium, it increases creep life because of its low diffusion rate, and it can be used as a partial rhenium substitute at lower concentrations to reduce density while preserving creep resistance (Ref 33, 34). A drawback to high tungsten concentrations is its tendency to form tcp phases.

Tungsten is not a strong MC-type carbide former, but it has been observed to have a profound effect on the distribution of MC carbides in experiments on doped IN-100. Tungsten was demonstrated to cause a much more homogeneous distribution of MC carbides throughout the dendrites and interdendritic regions than occurred in undoped IN-100 or in IN-100 doped with other transition elements (Ref 19). The same study demonstrated that tungsten additions affect the composition of the carbides, making the MC carbides less predominantly TiC and richer in mo-

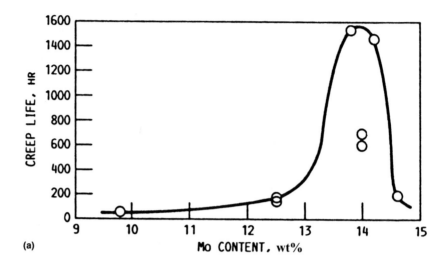

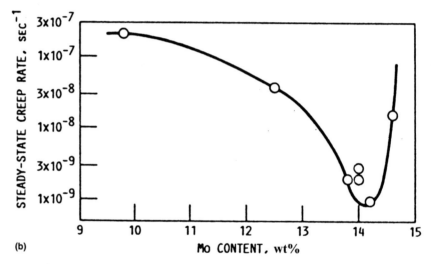

**Fig. 5.5** Influence of molybdenum in the 982 °C/234 MPa (1800 °F/34,000 psi) (a) creep life and (b) creep rate of an experimental single-crystal superalloy. Source: Ref 23

lybdenum, vanadium, and tungsten. It has also been observed that large amounts of tungsten can induce the carbide transformation from $M_{23}C_6$ to $M_6C$ (Ref 19, 31).

### 5.6.3 Niobium

Niobium was introduced as an alloying addition to superalloys in the 1940s with the development of S-816, a cobalt-base alloy containing 3 weight percent Nb. Although niobium can provide an even larger degree of solid-solution hardening than tungsten because of its large misfit in the

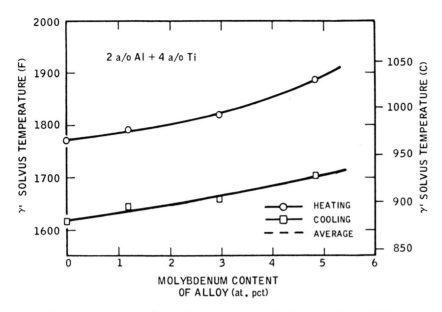

**Fig. 5.6** Influence of molybdenum content on γ′ solvus for a Ni-Cr-Al-Ti-Mo alloy. Source: Ref 27

**Table 5.10 Niobium-containing phases in superalloys**

| Symbol | Crystal type | Formula | Symbol | Crystal type | Formula |
|---|---|---|---|---|---|
| γ | Face-centered cubic (fcc) | Solid solution | $M_6C$ carbide | Complex cubic | $Fe_3Mo_3C$ |
| | | | | | $Fe_3W_3C$ |
| | | | | | $Fe_4W_2C$ |
| | | | | | $Fe_3Nb_3C$ |
| | | | | | $Nb_3Co_3C$ |
| | | | | | $Ta_3Co_3C$ |
| γ′ | Ordered fcc | $Ni_3(Al,Ti)$ | δ | Orthorhombic | $Ni_3Nb$ |
| γ″ | Ordered body-centered tetragonal | $Ni_3Nb$ | η | Hexagonally close-packed MC carbide | $Ni_3Ti$ Cubic |
| TiC | Laves | Hexagonal $MgZn_2$ | $Fe_2Nb$ | | |
| | | | | | $Fe_2Ti$ |
| | | | | | $Fe_2Mo$ |
| | | | | | $Fe_2Ta$ |
| | | | | | $Fe_2Ti$ |

Source: Ref 2

nickel lattice (Ref 2), its strengthening effects are attributable to precipitation hardening. Specifically, niobium is present in two types of strengthening phases, namely carbides (MC and $M_6C$) and γ″-$Ni_3Nb$, and can be present in other phases, as summarized in Table 5.10 (Ref 2). The phase fraction and stability of γ′ increases with niobium content, and at sufficient concentrations of niobium, γ″ precipitates. Niobium plays a significant role in strengthening low-coefficient-of-thermal-expansion superalloys in which chromium is not present.

Niobium is a strong carbide former, and the resulting stable niobium-containing carbides are instrumental in producing high creep strength (Ref 2). Substitution of molybdenum and niobium for titanium and aluminum in alloy IN-800H (Fe-21Cr-32Ni-0.4Ti-0.4Al) results in higher creep strength at temperatures ranging from 750 to 800 °C (1380 to 1470 °F) (Ref 37). This improvement is attributed to arrest of dislocation motion by NbC precipitates in the grains. In contrast to molybdenum, niobium retards the decomposition of primary MC carbides into $M_{23}C_6$- and $M_6C$-type carbides and impedes the growth of $M_{23}C_6$ carbides at the grain boundaries even after solution heat treatment at 1200 to 1260 °C (2190 to 2300 °F) (Ref 5). Niobium can also influence the formation of carbonitrides. In powder metal alloys, niobium suppresses the formation of carbonitrides along prior grain boundaries. It does this by reacting with carbon during the early stages of solidification and forming stable NbC particles, tying up the carbon necessary for carbonitride films to form on the powder surface at a later stage (Ref 2).

Niobium can also modify the behavior of the $\gamma'$ phase, because it tends to partition to this phase preferentially. Increasing niobium contents reduces the $\gamma'$ coarsening rate despite the concurrent increase in coherency strains (Ref 5) and can delay the $\gamma' \rightarrow \eta$ transformation in nickel-iron-base superalloys (Ref 24). Niobium partitions almost completely to the $\gamma'$ phase, resulting in an increase in the $\gamma'$ volume fraction.

Niobium has a negligible effect on oxidation resistance but significantly decreases hot corrosion resistance (Ref 2). Replacing molybdenum with niobium in IN-738, for example, drastically reduces hot corrosion resistance (Ref 28). The refractory elements molybdenum, tungsten, and niobium degrade hot corrosion resistance because they are quite reactive with $Na_2SO_4$; the reaction removes oxide ions, acidifying the surface layer, and oxides of the base metal are then dissolved. Niobium does not so strongly reinforce the mechanism of hot corrosion as molybdenum or tungsten, but it still makes the alloy more susceptible (Ref 38).

Niobium and tantalum can be used almost interchangeably in nickel-base superalloys, and their nominal concentration is often reported as combined niobium + tantalum. Properties for both niobium and tantalum are summarized in Table 5.11. Not surprisingly, these two elements have complete solubility in each other. The use of niobium is preferred to that of tantalum because of the former's lower density and cost. Despite their

Table 5.11  Properties of niobium and tantalum

| Property | Niobium | Tantalum |
|---|---|---|
| Crystal structure | Body-centered cubic | Body-centered cubic |
| Interatomic distance, nm | 0.2859 | 0.2860 |
| Atomic weight | 93 | 181 |
| Density, g/cm³ | 8.57 | 16.6 |
| Solubility in Co, at.% | 4 | 5 |
| Solubility in Fe, at.% | 2 | 2 |
| Solubility in Ni, at.% | 10 | 12 |
| Lattice mismatch in Co, % | 14.0 | 13.8 |
| Lattice mismatch in Fe, % | 10.8 | 10.6 |
| Lattice mismatch in Ni, % | 14.8 | 14.8 |
| Electron configuration | $4s^24p^64d^45s^1$ | $5s^25p^65d^35s^2$ |

Source: Ref 2

similarities, niobium and tantalum cannot always be substituted for each other. Substitution of tantalum for niobium in alloy 718 (Ref 2) reduces weld liquation cracking in the HAZ, because of the higher solubility of tantalum in nickel and its narrower solidification range. The substitution also raises the temperature capability of alloy 718. However, tantalum-containing alloy 718 is not commercially available because of the increased cost and weight associated with the substitution.

### 5.6.4 Tantalum

Tantalum was not a significant alloying element in most superalloys until the 1960s, when the literature on Russian superalloys was released. While the Americans and the British had been concentrating on aluminum and titanium as alloying additions, Russian metallurgists had been investigating the role of such refractory elements as tantalum, tungsten, and molybdenum (Ref 39). Subsequently, the first U.S. alloy to contain large amounts of tantalum was developed and designated as TRW-NASA VI A. This alloy was developed through computer optimization to maximize its creep-rupture strength. Unfortunately, such properties as stability, castability, and corrosion resistance were not considered during the early stages of its development.

Elemental tantalum has a bcc crystal structure and is highly mismatched to the nickel lattice. It acts as a strong solid-solution strengthener in both the $\gamma$ and $\gamma'$ phases and also provides strengthening through carbide formation (Ref 2, 40). It increases surface stability, specifically hot corrosion resistance, and tensile and creep strengths of both polycrystalline (Ref 40) and single-crystal (Ref 2) superalloys. Tantalum forms tantalum carbide, which has a very high melting point and thermodynamic stability, so tantalum provides additional strengthening at elevated temperatures (Ref 2). Tantalum exhibits strong partitioning toward the $\gamma'$ phase, with a nominal $\gamma/\gamma'$ partitioning ratio of 1 to 8 (Ref 23). This preferential partitioning increases alloy strength by affecting the $\gamma'$ precipitate and by increasing the energy necessary for dislocations to cut through the $\gamma'$ particles (Ref 39).

Typically, approximately 75 percent of the tantalum in an alloy partitions to the $\gamma'$ phase, up to 15 percent forms TaC, and the remainder partitions to the $\gamma$ matrix (Ref 41). Tantalum also hinders MC carbide decomposition in superalloys in a manner similar to niobium. It also segregates to the interdendritic region (Ref 42) during solidification, improving the hot tearing behavior of directionally solidified alloys (see section 5.5, "Titanium," in this chapter).

The role of tantalum in single-crystal superalloys differs from that in polycrystalline alloys due to lower or nonexistent levels of carbon and other grain-boundary elements. The absence of carbon and other grain-boundary elements causes tantalum to partition primarily to the $\gamma/\gamma'$ interdendritic liquid (Ref 40). In single-crystal alloys, tantalum is used in place of titanium to a significant extent because it simultaneously strengthens the $\gamma'$ phase and raises the solidus temperature (Ref 4). The absence of carbon also increases the amount of "effective tantalum" available in the alloy, which increases the incipient melting temperature. However, this increased incipient melting temperature may also be related to the absence of carbon, which is a melting-point depressant. Higher incipient melting temperatures in general mean that heat treatments can be carried out at higher temperatures, permitting a better control of $\gamma'$ size and distribution (Ref 40). The result is improved creep resistance and other high-temperature mechanical properties. Hot corrosion resistance is not degraded by tantalum, which differs from the other refractory metals of tungsten, niobium, and molybdenum (Ref 38). Reducing tantalum levels in single-crystal superalloys with a composition similar to MAR-M 247 (3 weight percent Ta) results in a reduction in the $\gamma'$ solvus temperature and volume fraction, tensile strength, and creep resistance.

The segregation of tantalum to the interdendritic liquid region and its high density has been observed to reduce the freckling in single-crystal superalloys. Due to the preferential partitioning of other refractories to the dendritic $\gamma$ phase, the interdendritic liquid tends to have a low density. It therefore rises to the top of the mushy zone, where it fractures the tips of dendrite arms, causing nucleation sites for freckling (chains of equiaxed grains) (Ref 20, 43). The presence of tantalum in the interdendritic liquid increases its density and reduces the propensity to fracture the dendrite tips.

In general, tantalum is one of the most important elemental additions in single-crystal superalloys, as indicated by the high tantalum levels (4 to 12 weight percent) in these alloys. These high levels have resulted in increased density (Ref 2) and higher costs (Ref 39).

### 5.6.5 Rhenium

Rhenium produces several beneficial effects in superalloys. This large, heavy element partitions preferentially to the $\gamma$ matrix (Ref 20, 33, 34, 44), providing strengthening through solid-solution hardening at high temperatures. It also increases the melting temperature of the alloy (Ref 33, 34). In addition to providing solid-solution hardening to the matrix phase, rhenium also influences the lattice parameters. It increases the $\gamma/\gamma'$ misfit, leading to additional strengthening (Ref 33, 34). This lattice mismatch also changes $\gamma'$ morphology upon isothermal aging, favoring the formation of fine, cuboidal, and aligned $\gamma'$ precipitates. Despite its influence on the size, shape, and distribution of $\gamma'$, rhenium does not have much influence on the $\gamma'$ volume fraction.

The main purpose of rhenium addition is to increase the creep life of both polycrystalline (Ref 44) and monocrystalline (Ref 4) superalloys. Rhenium addition of three percent (for example, oxide-dispersion-strengthened alloy 92) can double the creep-rupture life as compared to that of an alloy with the same nominal composition but without rhenium (Ref 44). Rhenium addition is found to retard $\gamma'$ coarsening through an increase in the activation energy of the particle-coarsening process. It is suggested that because rhenium strongly partitions to the $\gamma$ matrix, it is necessary for rhenium to diffuse from the $\gamma$ phase to allow the growth of $\gamma'$. Rhenium is known to have a very low diffusion rate in the superalloy matrix due to its large size. It is the diffusion of rhenium away from the $\gamma/\gamma'$ interface that limits the diffusion-controlled $\gamma'$ coarsening process (Ref 4) in alloys with rhenium content.

Second-generation single-crystal superalloys, introduced in the late 1980s, contained additions of rhenium to retard $\gamma'$ precipitate coarsening (Ref 4). This produced improvements in creep strength, particularly at very high temperatures of 1000 to 1150 °C (1830 to 2100 °F). Rhenium also appears to be associated with cluster formation in the matrix. The effect of rhenium on improving creep resistance is so strong that columnar-grained alloys containing rhenium have replaced some first-generation (nonrhenium) single-crystal superalloys, which results in significant cost-savings through the higher casting yields obtained with columnar-growth versus single-crystal components (Ref 45).

Like other refractories, rhenium additions are limited by tcp-phase formation, mainly the $\sigma$ and $\mu$ phases (Ref 4). Rhenium tends to replace chromium in the tcp phase rather than occupy other positions favored by refractories such as molybdenum and tungsten. It also causes hcp $\delta$-phase dendrites to precipitate in nickel-base superalloys. The stability of the $\delta$ phase is increased by high levels of aluminum + tantalum (16.5 to 21 atomic percent) (Ref 32, 46, 47), and its formation is altogether suppressed by a ruthenium addition of six atomic percent.

Rhenium degrades the oxidation resistance of nickel-base superalloys with low aluminum concentration (Ref 48), probably through the formation of volatile $Re_2O_7$ above 1000 °C (1830 °F). Rhenium prevents the formation of a fully dense protective alumina scale, making the scale more permeable to oxygen and also more likely to spall. This is only observed at low aluminum levels in the Ni-Cr-Al-Ti-Re system.

Rhenium has been successfully used as a component of a diffusion-barrier bilayer coating system that was demonstrated to offer excellent oxidation resistance on rhenium-containing alloys TMS-82 and CMSX-4 (Ref 49). A duplex coating system was used that consisted of an inner layer of rhenium, chromium, tungsten, and nickel and an outer layer of nickel, chromium, and aluminum. The inner layer was found to be more stable after extended high-temperature exposure than barrier compounds such as TiN, AlN, SiC, AlON, $ZrO_2$, and $Al_2O_3$ or elements such as iridium, rhenium, and tungsten. Very high rhenium concentrations were used in the diffusion barrier coating (30 to 38 percent), and it was found to be a very effective barrier both to the inward diffusion of aluminum and to the outward diffusion of nickel. The outer nickel, chromium, and aluminum layer provides the oxidation resistance (Ref 49).

### 5.6.6 Ruthenium

The role of ruthenium is very similar to that of rhenium, both in its properties and in its alloying effects. Each is completely soluble in the other (Ref 32). Like rhenium, ruthenium segregates to the γ dendrite cores but not as strongly as rhenium or tungsten (Ref 42, 50). A ruthenium level of three percent in a γ'-forming alloy prevents the formation of $M_6C$ carbides (of which tungsten is a main component) as compared to the ruthenium-free version of the same alloy (Ref 51). Ruthenium does not partition into the MC carbide formed but raises its precipitation temperature. It also lowers the formation temperatures of both eutectic and secondary γ'.

There is little information about the effects of large amounts of ruthenium on polycrystalline nickel-base superalloys. One study (Ref 42) on an experimental alloy, UM-F13, with the composition given in Table 5.12, containing 14.1 weight percent Re, shows that ruthenium addition induces the formation of a new phase (called the Heusler phase; Fig. 5.7) in addition to the hcp (rhenium, ruthenium) δ phase in rhenium/ruthenium-containing alloys. The ruthenium-rich Heusler phase forms in both the dendrites and interdendritic regions. The phase has an $L2_1$ structure ($a_H$ = 0.6089 nm), a formula of $Ru_2AlTa$, and is enveloped by the γ phase. This phase has also been reported by other investigators (Ref 52) and is notable for its low nickel solubility and high tantalum contents.

Ruthenium moderates the microsegregation that occurs during the solidification of single-crystal superalloys that contain refractory elements. Compositional gradients, which tend to occur on solidification of alloys with high refractory-element concentrations, are conducive to the formation of the deleterious tcp phases. A ruthenium concentration of four percent strongly counteracts the segregating behavior of such elements as chromium, rhenium, tungsten, and molybdenum (Ref 50). Ruthenium additions as low as one percent were shown to substantially reduce tcp-phase formation (Ref 53).

Counteracting the segregating tendency of the heavy refractory elements also reduces the formation of freckle defects (Ref 53), which are macroscopic defects formed by islands of high solute concentration as the solute is ejected to the interdendritic liquid during dendrite solidification.

Table 5.12  Chemical composition of the Heusler phase and the superalloy in which it forms

| | Chemical composition, at.% | | | | | | |
|---|---|---|---|---|---|---|---|
| | Ni | Al | Ru | Ta | Re | W | Co |
| Heusler phase | 7.21 | 31.77 | 44.96 | 12.92 | 0.11 | 2.01 | 1.01 |
| UM-F13 | 65.1 | 13.3 | 9.0 | 2.3 | 1.3 | 1.5 | 7.5 |

Source: Ref 42

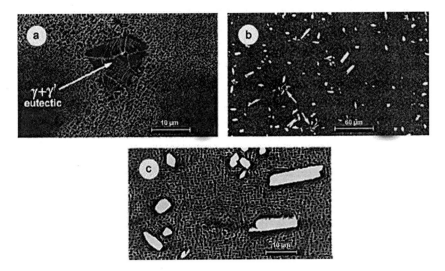

**Fig. 5.7** (a) Secondary electron image showing a γ/γ′ eutectic pool in as-cast UM-F13 alloy. (b) Backscattered electron image showing the typical microstructure of UM-F13 alloy after solution treatment at 1300 °C (2370 °F) for 4 h and aging at 1100 °C (2010 °F) for 100 h, which consists of γ (gray contrast), γ′ (dark contrast), and Heusler precipitates (white contrast). The clusters of Heusler precipitates are marked by arrows. (c) Higher-magnification image of (b)

Freckle formation is worst under slow solidification conditions, which allow large mushy zones and relatively long diffusion times, as would be the case in Bridgeman furnaces used for the casting of directionally solidified or single-crystal alloys. The tendency for freckles to form increases with increasing tungsten and rhenium but can be strongly reduced by the addition of ruthenium (Ref 53).

Ruthenium suppresses the precipitation and growth of tcp phases in single-crystal alloys after prolonged exposure to high temperatures and stabilizes the γ and γ′ microstructures. The effect is a significant improvement in creep life, particularly under conditions of low stress and high temperature, in alloy SRR300D (Ref 53).

In general, the addition of ruthenium allows for higher levels of other beneficial refractory elements with a great reduction in the deleterious effects of tcp-phase formation and the freckling associated with the segregating tendency of the heavy refractory elements.

## 5.7 Grain-Boundary Elements

The elements boron, carbon, zirconium, and, to a lesser extent, hafnium are added to superalloys to strengthen the grain boundaries by retarding relative motion between the grains. The common characteristic of these elements is their tendency to segregate toward the grain boundaries, mostly due to their unique sizes relative to the nickel matrix and their low solubility both in γ and γ′. The strengthening of the grain boundaries also enhances creep resistance, as shown in Table 5.13, by preventing the agglomeration of $M_{23}C_6$ carbides and grain-boundary $\gamma'$ and by preventing intergranular microcracking at grain boundaries transverse to the applied stress (Ref 12).

These elements are usually not needed in single-crystal superalloys (Ref 4), because these alloys are devoid of grain boundaries; moreover, these elements can strongly depress melting points. However, there is some evidence that these elements have certain beneficial effects in single-crystal superalloys. For example, the presence of carbide-forming grain-boundary strengtheners boron, carbon, and hafnium in nickel-base single-crystal superalloys decreases casting porosity (Ref 54), probably by increasing the tendency to form carbides, which reduces pore formation in the interdendritic regions. In addition, small amounts of grain-boundary strengtheners can diminish the drastic loss in strength that occurs in single-crystal superalloys with low- and high-angle grain-boundary defects by providing some strengthening at these subgrain boundaries. This permits higher levels of defects to be tolerated (with misorientations as high as 35 degrees) while still achieving similar creep resistance, hence increasing yield for single-crystal component manufacturing and reducing cost (Ref 45). This would be especially useful in stator manufacture, because the castings will have a higher occurrence of defects due to their complex shape.

Although they form similar compounds (borides and carbides) and have similar physical properties, the diffusion behavior of boron and carbon is significantly different (Ref 18). Experiments on boron-enriched alloy 690 (Ni-Cr-Fe) indicate that, after solution annealing, boron is enriched at the grain boundaries, while carbon is evenly distributed throughout the material. After heat treatment at 700 °C (1290 °F), precipitation of boron- and carbon-containing compounds is observed in the grain boundaries. This evolution in boron and carbon distribution is clearly shown in Fig. 5.8.

Hot tearing is a grain-boundary phenomenon, so elements that segregate to the grain boundaries, notably boron and zirconium, significantly influence hot tearing of columnar-grained nickel-base superalloys (Ref 22). Although these two elements can be tolerated individually to high levels without causing hot tearing (560 and 480 ppm, respectively), their co-presence, even at low concentrations, leads to significant hot tearing in columnar-grained IN-792. The effect is greater with increasing zirconium additions, even at low boron levels. This synergistic effect is thought to

**Table 5.13    Effect of boron and zirconium on creep of Udimet 500 at 870 °C (1600 °F)**

| Alloy | | $\sigma$ = 172 MPa (25 ksi) | | $\sigma$ for $\dot{\varepsilon}$ of 0.004% h | |
| --- | --- | --- | --- | --- | --- |
| | $\varepsilon$ in primary creep | Life, h | Elongation, 4D % | MPa | ksi |
| Udimet 500 | 0.002 | 5 | 2 | 117.2 | 17 |
| Udimet 500 + 0.19% Zr | 0.002 | 140 | 6 | 158.6 | 23 |
| Udimet 500 + 0.009% B | 0.002 | 400 | 8 | 193.1 | 28 |
| Udimet 500 + 0.009% B + 0.19% Zr | 0.002 | 647 | 14 | 220.6 | 32 |

Source: Ref 12

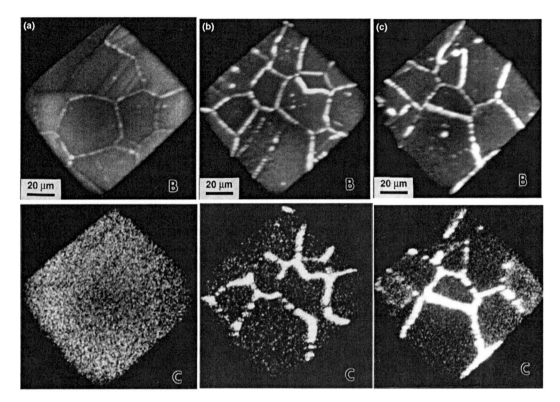

**Fig. 5.8** Secondary ion mass spectroscopy images showing boron (B) and carbon (C) concentration in boron-modified alloy 690. (a) Solution annealed. (b) Solution annealed + 700 °C (1290 °F)/1 h. (c) Solution annealed + 700 °C (1290 °F )/100 h. Source: Ref 42

occur through their influence on the solidus temperature of the alloy. Hot tearing depends on changes in the fraction of interdendritic liquid that result in high strains and strain rates during solidification. Boron and zirconium influence both the composition and the amount of interdendritic liquid, because they segregate to the interdendritic liquid during solidification (Ref 31, 55).

Despite their negative influence on hot tearing, additions of boron and zirconium improve the hot working and creep-rupture properties of all superalloys (nickel-iron, nickel, and cobalt base) (Ref 3, 7, 12). Addition of as little as 15 ppm of boron doubles both the rupture life and the ductility of Waspaloy. They also help to control impurity levels during processing; boron and zirconium prevent tramp elements such as oxygen and sulfur from collecting in the grain boundaries and forming brittle films (Ref 12).

### 5.7.1 Boron

In the late 1950s, the effect of boron on improving the creep properties and hot workability of superalloys was observed, which led to the use of boron as a strengthening element in the majority of nickel-base superalloys (Ref 56). In the 1980s, boron was demonstrated to be valuable in reducing the susceptibility of nickel-base alloys to grain-boundary attack in the temperature regime in which type II hot corrosion occurs (Ref 57).

Boron has a maximum solubility of approximately 0.2 weight percent in nickel, with higher levels leading to the formation of the intermetallic $Ni_3B$. Trace levels of boron, usually not more than 0.05 weight percent, can improve some nickel alloy properties, but higher levels cause the formation of brittle borides that can act as crack initiation sites. In addition to forming $Ni_3B$, boron can also combine with other elements, such as chromium, molybdenum, and zirconium, to form other brittle, high-melting-point intermetallic compounds (Ref 17). High boron levels (0.009 to 0.011 weight percent) in alloy 718 decrease the creep life of the alloy (Ref 56). Another detrimental effect of boron is its effect as a melting-point depressant, which effectively reduces the incipient melting temperature for the boron-rich regions of the alloy.

Trace levels of boron retard the deleterious transformation from $\gamma'$ to $\eta$. Equilibrium segregation of boron to the grain boundaries retards the nucleation of cells (Ref 5), with an accompanying increase in notched stress-rupture strength. Boron also has a slightly beneficial effect on the hot workability of Ni-(18–19)Cr-(20–22)W alloys (Ref 30). In concentrations of 0.010 to 0.015 percent, boron enhances the hot workability of wrought alloys and is generally added to the superalloy melt as NiB (Ref 27).

Boron is an active grain refiner (Ref 18, 58). In a study on an experimental nickel-aluminum two-phase ($\gamma$-$\gamma'$) alloy, boron doping of 0.5 atomic percent was shown to increase the yield strength slightly and increase the toughness by approximately one order of magnitude. The same study found that boron caused significant grain refinement. It is speculated that the segregation of boron to the grain boundaries retards grain growth, allowing more time for new grains to nucleate and increasing the time available for low-angle grain boundaries to anneal out. As a result, grain-boundary zones are formed in which the $\gamma'$ particles are much smaller than those outside the zone, and large $\gamma'$ particles are scattered along the grain boundary (Ref 58).

Other studies have yielded similar results. A similar grain-refining effect was found in a study of wrought alloys Udimet 710 and 720. These alloys have nearly identical composition except that Udimet 720 contains more boron and zirconium and less carbon. After identical processing, coarse $\gamma'$ was present in both alloys, but the Udimet 720 also contained a distribution of very fine $\gamma'$ (Ref 57). In experiments on alloy 690 with nominal composition of Ni-30Cr-9Fe (Ref 18), the boron-free alloy had a grain size of 111 μm after solution annealing, but the boron-containing alloy had a grain size of 60 μm. Carbon can also reduce grain growth during annealing, but its effect is not as pronounced as that of boron.

Another beneficial effect of boron is to reduce $M_{23}C_6$ carbide agglomeration, improving ductility. Boron can also reduce the solubility of carbon at the grain boundaries, increasing the amount of carbides at the grain boundaries while impeding the formation of coarse and continuous carbide layers. This effect is critically dependent on boron content; 50 ppm of boron is extremely favorable, but even slight increases above this amount prevent improvements in mechanical properties by forming low-melting-point borides (Ref 59).

Boron promotes dendritic solidification with numerous and thinner secondary dendritic arms in IN-738 (Ref 55), thereby increasing the surface area of interaction between solid and liquid during solidification. Boron strongly influences the formation of coarse $\gamma/\gamma'$ in the interdendritic area during the solidification of columnar-grained alloys (Ref 22), which is detrimental because it is harder to dissolve coarse $\gamma'$. High boron levels lower the solidus, limiting the temperature range available for heat treatment.

Boron at 100 ppm greatly increases stress-assisted grain-boundary oxidation resistance by promoting transgranular over intergranular fracture, as shown in Fig. 5.9 (Ref 60). In this study, the boron addition was achieved by a pack diffusion process, increasing the environmental resistance of the surface without jeopardizing the ductility of the bulk alloy. In Fig. 5.9(b), the transgranular fracture zone corresponds to an optimally enriched boron zone just below the surface. At depths in the sample where the boron enrichment is negligible, the fracture mode transitions to brittle intergranular, which is the same mode that predominates in the unmodified sample (Fig. 5.9a). The improved performance is due to the formation of (iron, nickel)-rich borides in the transgranular zone that seal the grain boundaries against oxygen penetration (Ref 60).

## 5.7.2 Carbon

Carbon contributes to the processing of superalloys in three ways:

- It acts as a refining agent during melting (deoxidizing and desulfurizing).
- It lowers the melting point and increases the fluidity of the liquid metal.
- It modifies the properties of the solidified metal.

As in steels, carbon plays a vital role in superalloys, even at low concentrations (less than one weight percent and commonly less than 0.1 weight percent). Its main effect on mechanical properties is strengthening via the formation of carbides, which is particularly significant in cobalt-base superalloys. Carbon, at levels of approximately 0.05 to 0.2 weight percent, combines with reactive and refractory elements such as titanium, tantalum, and hafnium to form primary MC carbides. During heat treatment and service, these MC carbides begin to transform into secondary carbides such as $M_{23}C_6$ and $M_6C$, which tend to populate the grain boundaries (Ref 5). In general, larger carbon contents are found in casting alloys than

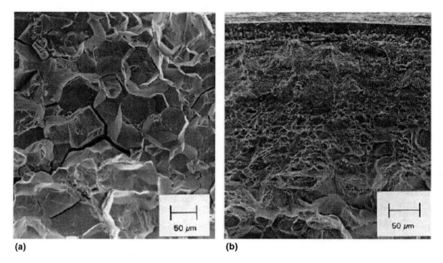

(a)                                        (b)

**Fig. 5.9** Scanning electron micrographs of the fracture surface of alloy 706 due to stress-assisted grain-boundary oxidation after constant strain-rate testing. (a) Brittle, intergranular fracture of unmodified alloy 706. (b) Transition zone of the boronized sample, showing a ductile transgranular fracture mode at the surface, transitioning to the bulk intergranular fracture mode. Source: Ref 18

wrought alloys (Table 5.1). Coarse primary carbides degrade hot workability, but carbon also depresses the solidus of nickel-base alloys and thereby improves their castability (Ref 45).

Carbon also plays an important role in liquid-phase processing, where carbon acts as a deoxidizer. The carbon remaining in the melt after deoxidation may immediately combine with refractory elements to form primary MC carbides or segregate to the interdendrite regions during solidification and form additional primary carbides. Some carbon is retained in solid solution in the alloy matrix and is therefore readily available for secondary carbide precipitation (Ref 45).

It has been found that premature creep failure can occur if carbon content is reduced below 0.05 weight percent in alloy 713LC, as shown in Fig. 5.10 (Ref 12, 45). Low carbon favors the precipitation of carbon-lean phases, for example, $M_6C$ and $M_2SC$, which may promote grain-boundary embrittlement. These latter particles, when extracted from the matrix of as-cast alloys, have flakelike morphologies with high aspect ratios, which are quite detrimental. Also, low carbon contents may result in inadequate deoxidation and desulfurization (Ref 12, 45).

The morphology of MC carbides is influenced by carbon levels, with increasing carbon forming scriptlike rather than blocky carbides (Ref 61). The formation of carbides also helps to decrease porosity in single-crystal superalloys. Carbon (up to 1.39 weight percent) decreases many types of defects in single-crystal superalloys, such as slivers, freckling, and porosity (Ref 43).

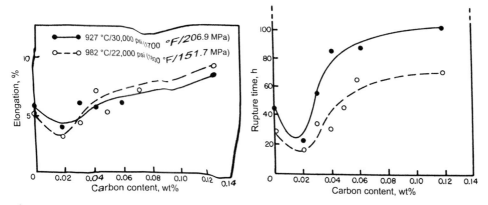

**Fig. 5.10** Effect of carbon on stress-rupture properties of alloy 713LC. Source: Ref 12

### 5.7.3 Zirconium

Zirconium, like boron, significantly enhances the creep properties of poly-crystalline superalloys, although when these two elements are used together, it is believed that boron is responsible for the property improvement, while zirconium plays the role of scavenger of tramp elements, notably sulfur (Ref 5). Zirconium has a very low solubility in nickel-base superalloys, so the residual interdendritic liquid tends to be zirconium rich (Ref 31). Zirconium tends to segregate to the grain boundaries, where, in trace amounts, it inhibits the agglomeration of $M_{23}C_6$ carbides and thus reduces the risk of microcrack formation. It can also inhibit grain growth at elevated temperatures (Ref 59).

Zirconium inhibits dendritic solidification in IN-738 and reduces the formation of secondary dendritic arms, thereby reducing the surface area for liquid/solid interaction (Ref 55), promoting cellular solidification with eutectic $\gamma/\gamma'$ nodules (Ref 12, 55).

Because zirconium is an effective melting-point depressant for nickel (Table 5.5), it promotes carbon and sulfur segregation to the grain boundaries by lowering the freezing point of the interdendritic liquid and increasing the temperature range between liquidus and solidus. Zirconium then combines with carbon and sulfur to form primary carbides and sulfocarbides, reducing the amount of carbon and sulfur in solid solution at the grain boundaries (Ref 12). Zirconium is also a strong desulfurizer, but this effect is used to a lesser extent in modern superalloys due to the lower impurity contents (Ref 22).

### 5.7.4 Hafnium

Hafnium has several beneficial effects on superalloy mechanical properties and environmental resistance as a result of its preferential location at grain boundaries (Ref 36). It was first used as an alloying element in superalloy systems to improve ductility without reducing creep resistance, which was achieved mainly by promoting a grain-boundary structure with a eutectic γ-γ' microstructure and finer carbides. Hafnium also has a high affinity for sulfur and acts as a getter. Hafnium strongly segregates to the interdendritic regions during solidification because of its low solubility in both the γ' and γ phases, although it has a higher solubility in γ' than γ (Ref 5, 12).

This interdendritic segregation behavior during solidification increases the volume fraction of blocky or massive γ' and eutectic γ/γ' at the grain boundaries, which improves the mechanical properties in the region, because stress concentrations occurring at the grain-boundary carbides can be relaxed more easily by fine slip in this γ' than by coarse slip in the γ matrix (Ref 45). The convoluted γ/γ' structure formed at the grain boundary is also a barrier to rapid crack propagation (Ref 5) and grain-boundary sliding (Ref 20). The effect of hafnium is not limited to modifying the γ/γ' morphology; it can also increase the hardness and resistance to cracking of γ' (Ref 5, 45, 62).

Hafnium additions also have an effect on carbide morphology, which provides an additional mechanism for improving alloy mechanical properties. Hafnium is a very strong carbide former, and it modifies the primary MC carbide from a scriptlike morphology to a small, blocky, discrete form that is more resistant to crack propagation than continuous scriptlike networks (Ref 5, 12, 45). The high affinity of hafnium for carbon also causes additional MC carbide precipitation at low carbon concentrations, at which precipitation would otherwise tend to cease. The resulting reduced carbon in solid solution in the grain-boundary region inhibits secondary $M_{23}C_6$ and $M_6C$ carbide precipitation.

The combined effect of hafnium on γ' and carbide morphology at the grain boundaries improves alloy strength, ductility, and creep resistance, as is evident from Table 5.14, where the performance of alloy MM 004, a 1.5 percent Hf version of alloy 713LC, is compared to alloy 713LC. Its effect on improving creep ductility has led to its widespread use in columnar-grained superalloys (Ref 4). Hafnium also reduces hot tearing in columnar-grained nickel-base alloys (Ref 5).

Hafnium increases resistance to sulfidation (a form of hot corrosion). It also increases the oxidation resistance of the base alloy (Ref 5) in a man-

**Table 5.14  Comparison of mechanical properties of alloys 713LC and MM 004 (1.5% Hf-modified alloy 713LC) in specimens taken from the rim and hub sections of an integrally cast turbine wheel**

| Alloy | Location | Tensile 20 °C (70 °F) | | | Tensile 760 °C (1400 °F) | | | 760 °C/586 MPa creep rupture | |
|---|---|---|---|---|---|---|---|---|---|
| | | 0.2% σY, MPa | Ultimate tensile strength, MPa | Elongation, % | 0.2% σY, MPa | Ultimate tensile strength, MPa | Elongation, % | Life, h | Elongation, % |
| 713LC | Rim | 696 | 758 | 7 | 648 | 786 | 4 | 38 | 1.9 |
| 713LC | Hub | 662 | 689 | 4 | 634 | 786 | 4.5 | 23 | 1.3 |
| MM 004 | Rim | 738 | 965 | 11 | 627 | 896 | 11 | 62 | 2.2 |
| MM 004 | Hub | 689 | 841 | 11 | 655 | 855 | 8 | 90 | 3.9 |

Source: Ref 12

ner similar to that of yttrium. This fact has been exploited in the CMSX series of alloys, where CMSX-2 is modified with a 0.1 atomic percent Hf addition and commercialized as CMSX-3, to improve aluminide coating adherence (Ref 39). The solutionizing temperature of CMSX-3 is lower than that of CMSX-2 because hafnium reduces the solidus temperature.

Hafnium is a strong melting-point depressant (Ref 22, 62). B-1900 has an incipient melting point of 1260 °C (2300 °F), but the same alloy modified with 1.5 weight percent Hf has an incipient melting point of 1220 °C (2230 °F) (Ref 1). This effect is one of the main disadvantages of the use of hafnium in single-crystal superalloys; not only does it reduce overall alloy temperature capabilities, but it also lowers solutionizing temperatures, which limits subsequent heat treatments to homogenize the alloy and dissolve coarse γ′ precipitates (Ref 22). Another disadvantage to the use of hafnium is its high reactivity (Ref 5, 22). During casting, it can react with ceramic molds and form brittle hafnium compounds that can become inclusions in the cast component (Ref 22).

Hafnium also has a high affinity for sulfur, so it can be used as a scavenger to prevent grain-boundary embrittlement caused by sulfur, because any excessive hafnium will partition to γ′, with a beneficial effect. Its use as a scavenging element can obviate the need to add other getter elements such as zirconium (Ref 12).

## 5.8 Reactive Elements

The role of reactive elements in superalloys is almost entirely for improving resistance to oxidation and hot corrosion through the reactive-element effect. The main elements added to superalloys to achieve this effect are yttrium (Haynes 214), lanthanum (HA-188), and cerium (Nimonic 86). Hafnium also causes this effect, but as discussed previously, it is used primarily for improving mechanical properties.

Of course, not all reactive elements improve environmental resistance to the same degree. Generally, yttrium is considered the most beneficial addition for improving oxidation resistance. However, in CMSX-4, lanthanum + yttrium additions are more effective than either element added alone, as illustrated in Fig. 5.11 (Ref 63). Cerium additions are also superior to lanthanum and yttrium in improving oxidation resistance. Overall, reactive-element additions improve the oxidation lifetime of the alloy by a factor of 10.

Yttrium and other reactive elements also increase the hot workability of Ni-Cr-W alloys and stainless steels (Ref 30), probably due to their roles as sulfur getters.

### 5.8.1 Reactive-Element Effect

The reactive-element effect was patented in 1937 (Ref 64, 65) and was first observed in the addition of rare earth metals to Nichrome as melt de-

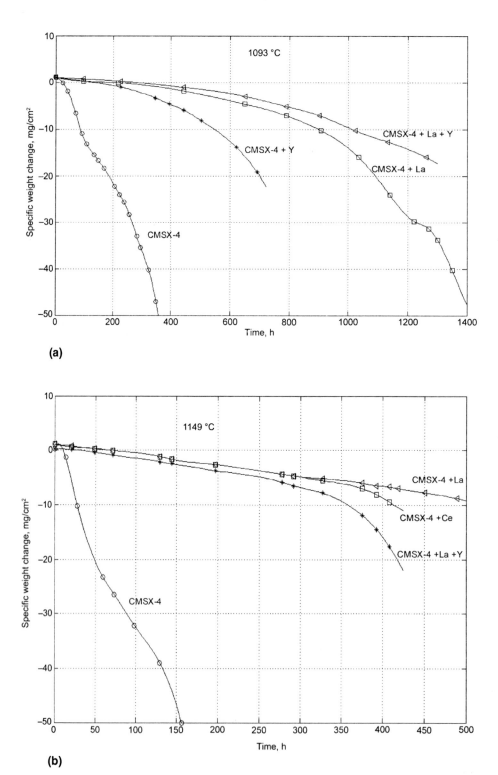

**Fig. 5.11** Dynamic oxidation results for reactive-element-modified CMSX-4 at (a) 1093 °C (2000 °F) and (b) 1149 °C (2100 °F). Source: Ref 12

oxidants. It was found that the addition of certain elements that react strongly with oxygen, even in trace amounts, can greatly increase the oxidation resistance of an alloy. The original patent covered elemental additions of yttrium and scandium, but it was later observed that oxides, hydroxides, and other salts containing the same elements also improve oxidation resistance (Ref 65). The beneficial effect of the reactive-element addition is independent of whether the element is added as an elemental addition or as an oxide in an oxide-dispersion-strengthened mechanically alloyed material. Elements from groups II through V of the periodic table can be used, although their effectiveness decreases moving from group II to V but increases with increasing atomic mass within a particular group (Ref 65). Today, the reactive elements typically used are yttrium, cerium, and lanthanum (Ref 66), and a small amount of any of these can lead to the formation of more adherent surface oxide scales (Ref 67, 68).

Generally, the reactive-element effect seems to be more remarkable in chromia-forming alloys, except for yttrium, which has a more significant effect in alumina-forming alloys (Ref 69, 70). Reactive elements are believed to influence the transport process for alumina scales by suppressing outward cation transport (Ref 70), which results in an inward growth of the oxide scale as opposed to a combined inward and outward growth observed on reactive-element-free alloys. The beneficial effects of reactive-element-doped systems can be grouped into two broad macroscopic effects: oxide scale adhesion and modification of the oxide scale growth mechanism.

The improved oxide scale adhesion may be related to three morphological features:

- Reduction of voids at the oxide/substrate interface, which is greatly reduced in chromia-forming alloys and almost completely suppressed in alumina-forming alloys (Ref 65)
- Increased smoothness of the alumina scale at the interface
- Appearance of stringers or pegs of $Sc_2O_3$ or $Y_2O_3$ (Ref 65)

Nonadherent alumina scales formed on reactive-element-free alloys have a dimpled surface with numerous filamentary protrusions and ridges ("pegs"). The formation of inward-growing oxide pegs with the addition of reactive elements mechanically keys the oxide scale to the alloy surface and thus reduces spalling (Ref 6, 65). In the presence of sulfur, the adherence of the alumina layer is thought to be further improved through the formation of a reactive-element sulfide in the alloy, which prevents sulfur segregation (Ref 69).

The modification of the growth mechanism(s) of the protective oxide scale occurs by the reactive element promoting the selective oxidation of the scale-forming element, and, as a result, a protective scale forms at lower concentrations of that element. Reactive elements suppress short-circuit aluminum transport (Ref 68, 69), and the scale grows by inward transport of oxygen as opposed to the outward transport of aluminum through the scale (Ref 6, 68, 70). The reactive element forms an oxide garnet, through which oxygen diffusion is slower than through the alumina scale. The oxide garnet may also retard crack propagation within the scale (Ref 69). The presence of the reactive element may also encourage the reformation of alumina after spalling from alloys, which otherwise would form spinels or other faster-growing oxides (Ref 6).

### 5.8.2 Yttrium

The main effect of yttrium is to improve oxidation lifetime. It can also improve an alloy resistance to other forms of environmental attack. A notable characteristic of yttrium (and other reactive-element) additions is the low percentage necessary to achieve the improvements in performance, often in trace amounts. Yttrium additions in the amount of less than 0.1 weight percent have been shown to improve the stress-assisted grain-boundary oxidation behavior of low-expansion superalloys. The mechanisms are not clear, but the formation of rod- and platelike nickel- and iron-rich intergranular precipitates is believed to be a factor (Ref 71). No yttrium was detected in these precipitates, but this may be due to the limitations of the detection methods, such as energy-dispersive x-ray analysis.

Yttrium is believed to interact with sulfur, forming yttrium oxysulfide ($Y_2O_2S_2$), thus preventing sulfur from interfering with the adherence of the protective oxide scale (Ref 63). The concentration of yttrium necessary to bind with the sulfur scales with the sulfur concentration, but yttrium has very low solubility in nickel, and even levels of 30 ppm can be above the solubility limit in some single-crystal superalloys, such as CMSX-4. When this limit is exceeded, nickel and yttrium form a series of eutectics that increase the risk of incipient melting.

Besides the inherent problem of low solubility in the nickel matrix and high reactivity, the addition of yttrium to superalloys has several drawbacks. Yttrium losses due to evaporation from the melt, reaction with the mold, and reaction with core material (for blades with internal cooling passages) require that the melt have a higher yttrium level than that desired for the final alloy composition, which introduces complications for reproducible compositional control. Overall, the highest source of yttrium loss is interaction with the mold and core materials. In the casting of single-crystal PWA 1484, it has been reported that only 10 percent of the yttrium added to the charge is retained in the final alloy composition, the rest being lost to the ceramic mold material and vaporization (Ref 63).

The improvement in oxide scale adherence can have additional consequences. For example, it can improve the adherence of the ceramic layer in thermal barrier coating systems, a phenomenon that has been observed with yttrium additions to CMSX-4 (Ref 63).

### 5.8.3 Lanthanum

Lanthanum is added to superalloys for the same reason yttrium is added, which is to improve oxidation resistance. The advantage of lanthanum over yttrium is that more of it is retained during casting (Ref 63). Additionally, when added in combination with yttrium, it helps to increase overall yttrium plus lanthanum retention. Like yttrium, the main source of lanthanum loss seems to be reaction with ceramic molds and cores.

## 5.9 Oxides

Oxide additions to superalloys, at levels of approximately one weight percent, are mainly used to provide strengthening and creep resistance in mechanically alloyed (MA) oxide-dispersion-strengthened (ODS) alloys. In practice, only nickel-base alloys are ODS, although the principle also applies to cobalt-base alloys. The type of oxide most commonly used in MA oxide-dispersion-strengthened alloys is yttrium oxide ($Y_2O_3$). Yttrium oxide cannot be introduced to the alloy as a fine dispersion by any means other than mechanical alloying. The MA alloys, which rely on powder metallurgy, have very fine grain structures and exhibit superplasticity. After grain coarsening, very high creep-rupture strengths can also be achieved at temperatures up to 90 percent of their homologous temperature (Ref 20).

Oxide dispersions can also improve the environmental resistance of an alloy, where reactive-element oxides are found to improve the oxide scale adhesion (Ref 16, 68). The effect is generally the same as if the reactive element were added directly. It is thought that the oxide particles (Ref 65, 69, 72) act as nuclei to favor the growth of alumina. On ODS coatings, the initial scale growth is much smoother and with fewer nodules than that of the scale on alloys of the same composition without oxide additions (Ref 70). Grain size of the oxide in dispersion-containing material has been found to be between five or ten times smaller than that in dispersion-free material, because the fine dispersion of oxide particles serve as nucleation sites for the development of an oxide layer at the surface of the material. The many distributed oxide-particle nucleation sites promote the rapid formation of a continuous fine-grained protective oxide layer. One study on a cobalt-base alloy demonstrated that a continuous protective $Cr_2O_3$ layer could form at lower chromium levels with oxide dispersions than without them (Ref 65).

Uniform distribution of the reactive-element oxide seems to be essential in improving the oxidation behavior (Ref 16). It has been postulated that if the reactive-element oxide suppresses aluminum cation diffusion through alumina, then it may also diminish the transport of other cations, such as nickel and iron, that form spinel oxides at the oxide scale. Essentially, the suppression of outward growth promotes selective oxidation of aluminum (Ref 70).

In nickel-chromium alloys, a number of dispersed oxides, including $Y_2O_3$, $La_2O_3$, $Al_2O_3$, $CeO_2$, $Sm_2O_3$, and $ThO_2$ have a beneficial effect on oxidation resistance. The one reactive metal oxide that does not is $Li_2O$ (Ref 65).

In cobalt-chromium alloys, the addition of one weight percent of elemental titanium, zirconium, and hafnium had no effect on oxidation resistance, but an addition of 0.1 weight percent Y enhanced the oxidation resistance significantly. However, dispersions of the oxides of titanium, zirconium, and hafnium were found to enhance the oxidation resistance (Ref 65).

## 5.10 Trace Elements

Trace elements are those elements present in superalloys in amounts so small that they are not reported in the nominal alloy composition and are often not reported in the literature unless the concentration of impurities is specifically being discussed. Most trace elements are not intentionally added to alloy melts, and most are detrimental; some of these elements are added to control the effects of other elements and are necessary. The development of vacuum melting and casting techniques, combined with higher purity in the charge materials, has led to a reduction in the levels of these elements in modern alloy production.

The presence of trace elements, intentional or not, can have a great effect on alloy casting and forging operations as well as on ductility, strength, fatigue life, and environmental resistance. These elements are tightly controlled, as shown in Table 5.15. For example, the fatigue life of alloy 625,

**Table 5.15  Allowable trace-element concentrations for selected nickel-base superalloys**

| | IN-718/MAR-M-247, typical alloy concentration | | | | | |
|---|---|---|---|---|---|---|
| | **Commercial grade** | | | | | |
| Element | **Tooling applications** | **Other** | **Aerospace quality** | | **Premium quality** | |
| N, ppm | 20+ | 60–100 | 60 | 5–15 | 10–25 | 1 |
| O, ppm | 5+ | 5–10 | <5 | <5 | 2 | 1 |
| Si, wt% | 0.05+ | 0.10–0.30 wt% | 0.05–0.10 | 0.02–0.04 | <0.02 | 0.008 |
| Mn, wt% | 0.01+ | 0.05+ | <0.02 | <0.002 | <0.002 | <0.002 |
| S, ppm | 15+ | 10–40 | 10–30 | 5–15 | 10 | <5 |
| Zr, wt% | ... | <0.01 | 0.001 | ... | <10 ppm | ... |
| Fe, wt% | 0.10+ | ... | ... | 0.05–0.10 | ... | 0.03 |
| Cu, wt% | 0.002+ | 0.08 | 0.01–0.05 | 0.002–0.005 | <0.001 | <0.001 |
| P, wt% | 0.002 | 0.005 | 0.005 | <0.005 | 0.001–0.002 | <0.001 |
| Pb, ppm | <1 | 1–5 | <1 | <1 | <1 | <0.5 |
| Ag, ppm | <0.5 | <1 | <1 | <0.5 | <0.5 | <0.5 |
| Bi, ppm | <0.3 | <0.5 | <0.5 | <0.3 | <0.2 | <0.2 |
| Se, ppm | <0.5 | <1 | <1 | <0.5 | <0.5 | <0.5 |
| Te, ppm | <0.3 | <0.5 | <0.5 | <0.2 | <0.2 | <0.2 |
| Tl, ppm | <0.3 | <0.5 | <0.5 | <0.2 | <0.2 | <0.2 |
| Sn, ppm | <5 | 15–40 | <10 | <5 | <10 | <5 |
| Sb, ppm | <2 | 2+ | <2 | <1 | <2 | <1 |
| As, ppm | <2 | 5 | <2 | <1 | <2 | <1 |
| Zn, ppm | <2 | 2+ | <2 | <1 | <2 | <1 |

Note: + = or higher. Source: Ref 1

a highly corrosion-resistant solid-solution-hardened superalloy, can be increased significantly by tighter controls during manufacturing of three trace elements, carbon, silicon, and nitrogen, as shown in Fig. 5.12.

These trace elements can be grouped into three broad categories: residual gases introduced during casting or atomizing operations, residual nonmetals, and residual metals and metalloids.

### 5.10.1 Trace Gases

Trace gases, such as oxygen, hydrogen, nitrogen, argon, and helium, may be present in superalloys after casting and generally have a deleterious effect. These gases are introduced into the alloy by interactions with the atmosphere, either during charge melting or during powder atomization or handling. Nitrogen and hydrogen are considerably harmful to malleability, even in minute additions. Trace amounts of oxygen (above 50 ppm) can significantly reduce the stress-rupture life of cast and powder alloys, as shown in Fig. 5.13 (Ref 12). Oxygen and nitrogen also cause grain-boundary embrittlement through the formation of nitrides or oxides. Ni-

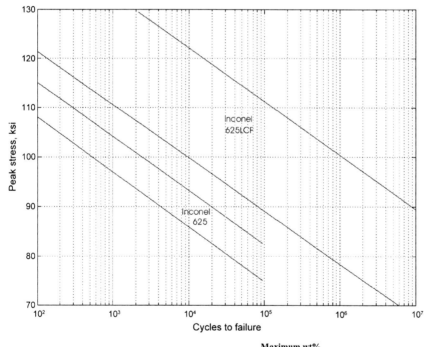

| | Maximum wt% | |
|---|---|---|
| Trace element | IN-625 | IN-625LCF |
| C | 0.1 | 0.03 |
| Si | 0.5 | 0.15 |
| N | Not specified | 0.02 |

**Fig. 5.12** Effects of trace-element control on fatigue life of alloy 625. Source: Ref 65

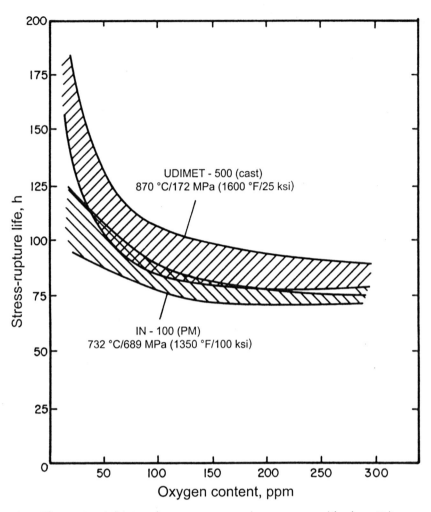

**Fig. 5.13** Influence of oxygen content on the stress-rupture life of cast Udimet 500 and powder metallurgy IN-100. Source: Ref 12

trogen and titanium react to form brittle particles that provide nuclei for the precipitation of MC carbides, which reduce ductility. Nitrogen can also dissolve in MC and $M_6C$ to form carbonitrides, further embrittling the grain boundaries. For a given carbon content, increasing nitrogen contamination causes the formation of brittle particles that decrease malleability and ductility.

Another problem of trace gases is that they are soluble in the metal matrix. The solubility of hydrogen in nickel is approximately 40.7 ppm at 1600 °C (2910 °F) and 1 atm, while it is 10 ppm for nitrogen in nickel and 0.62 weight percent for oxygen in nickel (Ref 12). However, these solubilities increase with alloying content and temperature (24 weight percent Cr can increase the solubility of nitrogen in nickel from 10 to 1000 ppm) (Ref 12). Upon cooling, the combined effect of temperature and compositional segregation causes solubility to decrease, resulting in porosity in the casting/component as the gas escapes. In superalloy powders, small amounts of helium and argon dissolved in the melt prior to atomization may become entrapped in the liquid droplets (Ref 12).

If vacuum melting is not being used, nitrogen removal can be achieved through deoxidation, such as through an active CO boil or bubbling argon through the melt. Because of the high reactivity of nitrogen with elements such as titanium, aluminum, and niobium, it is not easily removed during vacuum melting and must be controlled by minimizing the nitrogen content of the charge (Ref 12).

In general, the trace gas content in superalloys has been reduced considerably by the adoption of vacuum melting/casting practices, but there are still some alloys that can be manufactured under air or argon atmosphere with much lower costs and consequent poorer performance due to their higher impurity levels.

### 5.10.2 Sulfur

Sulfur has been recognized as a detrimental element in iron alloys for over a century, and its effects are well documented (Ref 12, 73, 74). In iron alloys, sulfur readily combines with iron in the melt to form FeS, which is insoluble in solid iron; therefore, it separates to the grain boundaries upon solidification. FeS has very low shear strength and causes severe weakening of the alloy. In steelmaking, manganese is added to getter the sulfur by forming MnS, which floats as slag.

The detrimental effects of sulfur in nickel alloys was also long ago demonstrated and first described in a 1925 paper by Merica and Waltenburg (Ref 12, 75). As in iron alloys, sulfur forms at the grain boundaries because of its low solubility in solid nickel. The sulfur causes embrittlement during hot working because nickel-sulfur has a low-melting-point eutectic, and liquid would form at the grain boundaries during forging. The solution was the same as for iron alloys, that being the addition of manganese, which forms MnS particles at the grain boundaries and reduces the embrittling effect.

Today, there are strict limits on sulfur content in superalloys. The detrimental effects of sulfur include reduced fatigue life, creep resistance, workability, and adhesion of protective oxide scales. For example, sulfur in the range of 0.017 to 0.02 weight percent decreases the creep resistance of alloy 718 (Ref 56).

Titanium- and zirconium-rich sulfocarbides of the $M_2SC$ type have been studied in alloys 713LC and 100 (Ref 12). These phases crystallize as hexagonal flakes or plates in the terminal interdendritic liquid during the freezing of cast alloys or in the liquid grain-boundary pools of powder compacts exposed to supersolidus grain-growth treatments. Because MC carbide has a closely related crystal structure and similar chemical composition as these sulfocarbides, MC carbides will often precipitate epitaxially and coherently on these sulfocarbides. These sulfocarbides are detrimental because they act as crack initiation sites at very small plastic strains.

Sulfur in excess of 0.005 percent can decrease the malleability of nickel during hot forging at 1093 °C (2000 °F), which can be attributed to the low solubility of sulfur in nickel and the consequent formation of low-melting-point of 643 °C (1190 °F) intergranular eutectic phases. Additions of manganese and magnesium can reduce the formation of these phases by forming dispersions of MnS and MgS, respectively.

Sulfur in a superalloy is particularly detrimental to welding, because sulfur segregates to the fusion zone and forms sulfides that act as crack initiation sites, decreasing the resistance of the weld zone to hot cracking (Ref 12). Additions of zirconium effectively counteract sulfur. As shown in Fig. 5.14, the doping elements titanium, zirconium, hafnium, and lanthanum, which have low solubility in the γ phase and a high affinity for sulfur, improve ductility by forming primary sulfides and thereby reducing the amount of available sulfur in solid solution. The dopant concentration

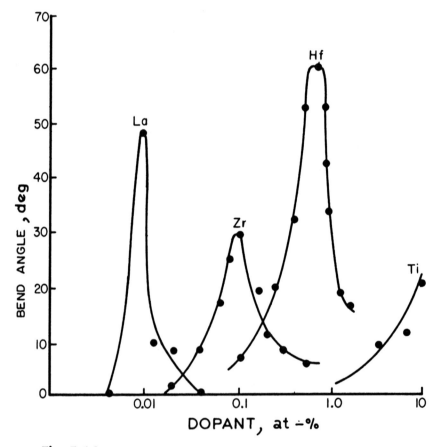

**Fig. 5.14** Alloy ductility variation with dopant additions. Source: Ref 12

must be carefully controlled, because at excessive levels intermetallic phases will form that will reduce ductility.

### 5.10.3 Phosphorus

Phosphorus is similar to sulfur in that it also has low solubility in nickel and forms low-melting-point eutectics of 875 °C (1610 °F), so it is reasonable to expect the same detrimental effects via the formation of intergranular liquid at high temperatures (Ref 12). However, recent studies, bucking "conventional wisdom," have shown that it can improve the creep resistance of some alloys, notably alloy 718, in which the creep rate was slowed by phosphorus doping in levels ranging between 0.016 and 0.020 weight percent (Ref 56, 76). The mechanism appears to be diffusion related, with phosphorus lowering the self-diffusion constant of nickel. Because phosphorus, like sulfur and boron, strongly segregates to the grain boundaries, small phosphorus additions tend to impede the self-diffusion of nickel across grain boundaries, thereby enhancing creep life (Ref 56).

Phosphorus addition in the range of 25 to 130 ppm (0.0010 to 0.0130 wt%) was also observed to increase the stress-rupture life, with no effect on microstructure or room-temperature tensile properties (Ref 76). At low levels, the stress-rupture life is prolonged, but at higher levels ductility is reduced. Phosphorus also has a significant effect on creep life, the maximum life being achieved at approximately 130 ppm. This implies that the main strengthening effect of phosphorus is to strengthen the grain boundary, in contrast to the grain interior. Favorable improvement is also observed with respect to crack propagation and fatigue life. In alloy 718, the addition of 0.008 weight percent P has been observed to increase the stress-rupture life up to 704 °C (1300 °F) (Ref 41, 77). Although this addition also improves ductility at 840 °C (1540 °F) as compared to undoped alloy 718, it decreases the ductility at higher temperatures. At these levels, no negative effect on the weldability of the alloy was observed.

It appears that phosphorus has a synergistic effect with boron and that combining them leads to higher creep resistance and stress-rupture life. In a modified alloy 718 with 0.005 percent C, 0.022 percent P, and 0.011 percent B, an increase in stress-rupture life between 200 and 300 percent was observed at 650 °C (1200 °F) (Ref 77). This effect is greater at lower temperatures and begins to decline above 704 °C (1300 °F). It is believed to be due to a phosphorus + boron strengthening effect on the $\gamma''$ phase, which loses strength above this temperature. Improvements in creep-rupture properties associated with boron and phosphorus appear to result from enhanced grain-boundary cohesion, segregation, and vacancy pinning effects that slow down processes such as diffusion and particle growth (Ref 78).

In contrast to the combined phosphorus plus boron effect, phosphorus plus sulfur interactions reduce creep resistance, probably through thermally activated grain-boundary diffusion processes. Most of these trace elements segregate strongly to the grain boundary and significantly reduce the surface energy at the grain boundary.

### 5.10.4 Trace Metals and Metalloids

This section discusses only those metallic and semimetallic elements that have not been previously discussed and do not normally occur in gaseous form.

Restrictions on the levels of these elements vary from element to element. The Society of Automotive Engineers Aerospace Material Specification (AMS) 2280 specifies maximum quantities of bismuth and tellurium of 0.5 ppm, selenium of 3 ppm, and lead and thallium of 5 ppm in nickel-base superalloy castings (Ref 12) and further specifies that the level of each of the following elements should not exceed 50 ppm, while the total amount must not exceed 400 ppm: antimony, arsenic, cadmium, gallium, germanium, gold, indium, mercury, potassium, silver, sodium, thorium, tin, uranium, and zinc (Ref 12). The effects of five of these elements can be seen in Fig. 5.15 and Fig. 5.16.

Some elements do not significantly diminish alloy properties when present in trace amounts. Trace additions of selenium (0.002 weight percent), tin, antimony, arsenic, silver, mercury (0.01 weight percent), cadmium (0.01 weight percent), indium, gallium, and germanium (0.1 weight percent) are not detrimental to the stress-rupture properties of IN-100 and may even increase the stress-rupture life of MAR-M 200 at 760 °C (1400 °F) (Ref 12).

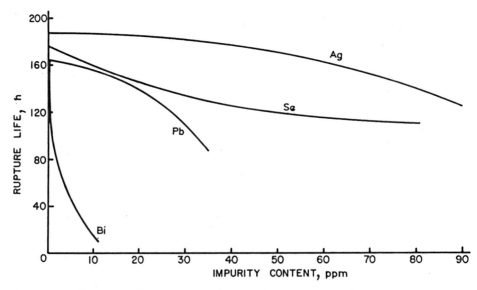

**Fig. 5.15** Effects of metallic impurities on the 649 °C/690 MPa (1200 °F/100,000 psi) stress-rupture life of Unitemp-718. Source: Ref 12

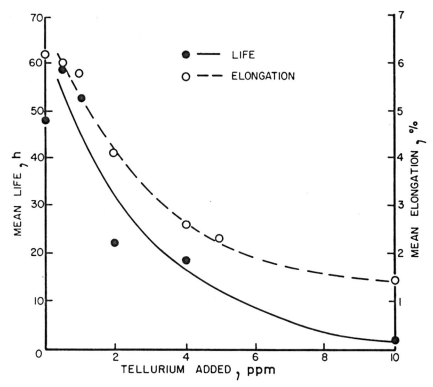

**Fig. 5.16** Decrease in fatigue life and ductility with increasing tellurium impurities. Source: Ref 12

Some trace elements are added intentionally to superalloys. Silicon and manganese are added to superalloys as refining additions during melting and processing, with silicon for deoxidizing and manganese to mitigate sulfur content (Ref 12). For example, raising silicon content from 0.15 to 0.4 weight percent in alloy 907 (resulting in alloy 909) permits the alloy to achieve higher toughness and strength with less stringent compositional controls and shorter heat treatment times (Ref 79). Moreover, silicon and manganese in concentrations of 0.46 and 0.93 weight percent, respectively, increase the weldability of Hastelloy X and alloy 718, because they segregate to the fusion zone in welds and reduce the tendency for hot cracking (Ref 12). In cobalt-base alloys, silicon and manganese are used for improving fluidity as well as for deoxidizing and sulfur control (Ref 3).

Despite some beneficial effects, the presence of trace elements in the final alloy is often considered detrimental, and upper limits on their concentrations are specified at low levels in most alloy specifications. According to AMS 5397, for example, the maximum allowable silicon + manganese content in IN-100 is 0.2 weight percent. A silicon level of one percent in alloy 718 causes the alloy to fragment during hot forging, and silicon levels between 0.2 and 0.8 percent reduce creep-rupture life at 650 °C/600 MPa (1200 °F/87,000 psi). In Ni-Cr-W alloys, silicon (0.5 percent) and manganese (one percent) greatly reduce hot workability (Ref 29). This effect also occurs in Hastelloy X and Inconel 600, in which copper also has the same effect.

Calcium and magnesium can also be added to superalloy melts as deoxidizers. Like silicon and manganese, they can have some other beneficial effects as well. Residual magnesium up to 37 ppm can increase the microfissure resistance of alloy 718 in weldability tests (Ref 12). Traces of calcium, magnesium, and rare earth elements can improve the hot workability and intermediate-temperature (650 °C, or 1200 °F) stress-rupture behavior of alloys such as alloy 718 (Ref 12, 40). Magnesium can reduce niobium segregation by decreasing the size of secondary dendrite arm spacing and interdendritic Laves and MC eutectic phases (Ref 2). Magnesium in the range of 0.01 to 0.05 weight percent can improve the malleability of wrought alloys by bonding to sulfur (Ref 5).

Depending on the alloy compositions and the amount of trace elements present, the effects on properties can vary. It is therefore important that each trace element be analyzed individually.

## REFERENCES

1. M.J. Donachie and S.J. Donachie, *Superalloys: A Technical Guide,* 2nd ed., ASM International, 2002
2. P. Kumar, The Role of Niobium and Tantalum in Superalloys, *Advances in High Temperature Structural Materials and Protective Coatings,* A.K. Koul, Ed., National Research Council of Canada, Ottawa, 1994, p 34–53
3. A.M. Beltran, Cobalt-Base Alloys, *Superalloys II,* C.T. Sims, N.S. Stoloff, and W.C. Hagel, Ed., John Wiley & Sons, 1987, p 135–163
4. M. Durand-Charre, *The Microstructure of Superalloys,* Gordon and Breach Science Publishers, Amsterdam, 1997, p 1–124
5. E.W. Ross and C.T. Sims, Nickel-Base Alloys, *Superalloys II,* C.T. Sims, N.S. Stoloff, and W.C. Hagel, Ed., John Wiley & Sons, 1987, p 97–133
6. I. Allam, D. Whittle, and J. Stringer, The Oxidation Behavior of CoCrAl Systems Containing Active Element Additions, *Oxid. Met.,* Vol 12 (No. 1), 1978, p 35–67
7. E.E. Brown and D.R. Muzkya, Nickel-Iron Alloys, *Superalloys II,* C.T. Sims, N.S. Stoloff, and W.C. Hagel, Ed., John Wiley & Sons, 1987, p 317–326
8. "Commodity Statistics and Information," U.S. Geological Survey, 2004, http://minerals.usgs.gov/minerals/pubs/commodity
9. R.L. Dreshfield, Evaluation of Mechanical Properties of a Low Cobalt Wrought Superalloy, *Superalloys 1992,* S.D. Antolovich et al., Ed., TMS, 1992, p 317–326
10. H. Murakami, T. Yamagata, H. Harada, and M. Yamazaki, The Influ-

ence of Co on Creep Deformation Anisotropy in Ni-Base Single Crystal Superalloys at Intermediate Temperatures, *Mater. Sci. Eng. A,* Vol 223, 1997, p 54–58

11. J.R. Mihalisin and D.L. Pasquine, Phase Transformations in Nickel-Base Superalloys, *Superalloys 1968,* TMS, 1968, p 134–170

12. R.T. Holt and W. Wallace, Impurities and Trace Elements in Nickel-Base Superalloys, *Int. Met. Rev.,* Vol 21, 1976, p 1–14

13. N. Birks, G. Meier, and F. Petit, Overview: Forming Continuous Alumina Scales to Protect Superalloys, *JOM,* Vol 46 (No. 12), 1994, p 42–46

14. S. Grisaffe, Coatings and Protection, *The Superalloys,* C.T. Sims and W.C. Hagel, Ed., Wiley Interscience, New York, 1972, p 341–370

15. N. Czech, F. Schmitz, and W. Stamm, Microstructural Analysis of the Role of Rhenium in Advanced MCrAlY Coatings, *Surf. Coat. Technol.,* Vol 76/77, 1995, p 28–33

16. R. Mevrel, State of the Art on High-Temperature Corrosion-Resistant Coatings, *Mater. Sci. Eng. A,* Vol 120, 1989, p 13–24

17. K.A. Ellison, P. Lowden, J. Liburdi, and D.H. Boone, "Repair Joints in Nickel-Based Superalloys with Improved Hot Corrosion Resistance," Paper 93-GT-247, ASME, 1993

18. M. Thuvander and K. Stiller, Microstructure of a Boron Containing High Purity Nickel-Based Alloy 690, *Mater. Sci. Eng. A,* Vol 281, 2000, p 96–103

19. P. Felix, in *Deposition and Corrosion in Gas Turbines,* A.B. Hart and J.B. Culter, Ed., Applied Science, London, 1972

20. C.T. Sims, Superalloys: Genesis and Character, *Superalloys II,* C.T. Sims, N.S. Stoloff, and W.C. Hagel, Ed., John Wiley & Sons, 1987, p 3–26

21. T. Totemeier, W. Gale, and J. King, Microstructural Evolution of an Overlay Coating on a Single-Crystal Nickel-Base Superalloy, *Metall. Mater. Trans. A,* Vol 25, 1994, p 2837

22. J. Zhang and R.F. Singer, Effect of Zr and B on Castability of Ni-Based Superalloy IN792, *Mater. Trans. A,* Vol 35, 2004, p 1337–1342

23. R.A. McKay, M.V. Nathal, and D.D. Pearson, Influence of Molybdenum on the Creep Properties of Nickel-Base Superalloy Single Crystals, *Metall. Trans. A,* Vol 21 (No. 2), 1990, p 381–388

24. T. Shibata, Y. Shudo, and Y. Yoshino, Effects of Aluminum, Titanium and Niobium on the Time-Temperature Precipitation Behavior of Alloy 706, *Superalloys 1996,* R.D. Kissinger et al., Ed., TMS, 1996, p 153–162

25. L. Heikinheimo, Repair Brazing of Gas Turbine Hot Parts—Methods and Joint Characterization, *VTT Symp.,* No. 211, 2001, p 149–162

26. M.B. Henderson, D. Arrell, M. Heobel, R. Larsson and G. Marchant, "Nickel-based Superalloy Welding Practices for Industrial Gas Tur-

bine Applications," University of Cambridge, 2002, p 1–14. http://www.msm.cam.ac.uk/phasetrans/2002/papers/APNickelWeldv2.pdf

27. W.T. Loomis, J.W. Freeman, and D.L. Sponseller, The Influence of Molybdenum on the γ' Phase in Experimental Nickel-Base Superalloys, *Metall. Trans.,* Vol 3, 1972, p 989–1000

28. J.P. Collier, P.W. Keefe, and J.K. Tien, The Effects of Replacing the Refractory Elements Tungsten, Niobium and Tantalum with Molybdenum in Nickel-Base Superalloys on Microstructural, Microchemistry and Mechanical Properties, *Metall. Trans. A,* Vol 17 (No. 4), 1986, p 651–661

29. J. Zhang, Effect of Ti and Ta on Hot Cracking Susceptibility of Directionally Solidified Ni-Based Superalloy IN792, *Scr. Mater.,* Vol 48 (No. 6), 2003, p 667–681

30. H. Tsuji, T. Shimizu, S. Isobe, and H. Nakajima, Effect of Minor Alloying Elements on Hot-Workability of Ni-Cr-W Superalloys, *J. Nucl. Sci. Technol.,* Vol 31 (No. 2), 1994, p 122–129

31. Y. Murata, K. Suga, and N. Yukawa, Effects of Transition Elements on the Properties of MCrAlY Carbides in IN-100 Nickel-Based Superalloy, *J. Mater. Sci.,* Vol 21 (No. 10), 1986, p 3653–3660

32. Q. Feng, T.K. Nandy, and T.M. Pollock, The Re(Ru)-Rich Delta-Phase in Ru-Containing Superalloys, *Mater. Sci. Eng. A,* Vol 373, 2004, p 239–249

33. S. Wollmer and U. Glatzel, Influence of Tungsten and Rhenium Concentration on Creep Properties of a Second Generation Superalloy, *Mater. Sci. Eng. A,* Vol 319–321, 2001, p 792–795

34. B. J. Piearcy and F. L. Versnyder, A New Development in Gas Turbine Materials: The Properties and Characteristics of PWA 664, *J. Aircr.,* Vol 3 (No. 5), 1966, p 390

35. X. Huang, "Course Notes: MECH 5803—Surface and Coatings," Carleton University, Ottawa, 2004

36. N.S. Stoloff, Fundamentals of Strengthening, *Superalloys II,* C.T. Sims, N.S. Stoloff, and W.C. Hagel, Ed., John Wiley & Sons, 1987, p 61–96

37. A. Doi, C. Asano, M. Sukekawa, and S. Kirihara, Effect of Niobium and Molybdenum on Creep Rupture Strength of 23Cr-34Ni-Fe Based Alloys, *Proc. International Conference on Creep,* April 1986, Japan Society of Mechanical Engineers, Tokyo, 1987, p 227–232

38. Y. Murata, K. Suga, and N. Yukawa, Effect of Transition Elements on the Properties of MC Carbides in IN-100 Nickel-Based Superalloy, *J. Mater. Sci.,* Vol 21, 1986, p 3653–3660

39. R.J. Quigg, Tantalum's Effect on Nickel-Base Superalloys, *Proc. International Symposium on Tantalum and Niobium,* Nov 1988, p 619–629

40. P.T. Ford, Tantalum in Superalloys, *Adv. Mater. Process.,* Vol 149 (No. 2), 1996, p 39–40

41. W.D. Cao, R.L. Kennedy, and W.M. Thomas, Stress-Rupture Strength of Alloy 718, *Adv. Mater. Process.,* Vol 149 (No. 3), 1996, p 33–36

42. Q. Feng, T.K. Nandy, and T.M. Pollock, Observation of a Ru-Rich Heusler Phase in a Multicomponent Ni-Base Superalloy, *Scr. Mater.,* Vol 50, 2004, p 849–854

43. K.A. Al-Jarba and G.E. Fuchs, Effect of Carbon Additions on the As-Cast Microstructure and Defect Formation of a Single Crystal Ni-Based Superalloy, *Mater. Sci. Eng. A,* Vol 373, 2004, p 255–267

44. H.S. Ko, K.W. Paik, L.J. Park, Y.G. Kim, and J.H. Tundermann, Influence of Rhenium on the Microstructures and Mechanical Properties of a Mechanically Alloyed Oxide Dispersion-Strengthened Nickel-Base Superalloy, *J. Mater. Sci.,* Vol 33, 1998, p 3361–3370

45. J.B. Wahl, K. Harris, and T.L. Moore, Grain Boundary Strengthened Single Crystal Superalloys, *Proc. Advanced Materials and Processes for Gas Turbines,* Sept 22–26, 2002, p 129–135

46. M.H. Vidal-Setif, M. Lancin, C. Marhic, R. Valle, J.L. Raviart, J.C. Daux, and M. Rabinovitch, On the Role of Brittle Interfacial Phases on the Mechanical Properties of Carbon Fibre Reinforced Al-Based Matrix Composites, *Mater. Sci. Eng. A,* 1999, p 321–333

47. Y.H. He, L.J. Chen, P.K. Liaw, R.L. McDaniels, C.R. Brooks, R.R. Seeley, and D.L. Klarstrom, Low-Cycle Fatigue Behavior of Haynes HR-120 Alloy, *Int. J. Fatigue,* Vol 24, 2002, p 931–942

48. M. Moniruzzaman, M. Maeda, Y. Murata, and M. Morinaga, Degradation of High-Temperature Oxidation Resistance for Ni-Based Alloys by Re Addition and the Optimization of Re/Al Content, *ISIJ Int.,* Vol 43 (No. 3), 2003, p 386–393

49. D. Sumoyama, K. Thosin, T. Nishimoto, et al., Formation of a Rhenium-Base Diffusion-Barrier-Coating System on a Ni-Base Single Crystal Superalloy and Its Stability at 1423 K, *Oxid. Met.,* Vol 68, 2007, p 313–329

50. R. Kearsey, "Compositional Effects of Microsegregation Behaviour in Single Crystal Superalloy Systems," Ph.D. thesis, Carleton University, 2004

51. L. Zheng, C.Q. Gu, and Y.R. Zheng, Investigation of the Solidification Behavior of a New Ru-Containing Cast Ni-Base Superalloy with High W Content, *Scr. Mater.,* Vol 50, 2004, p 435–439

52. B. Tryon, Q. Feng, and T. Pollock, Intermetallic Phases Formed by Ruthenium-Nickel Alloy Interdiffusion, *Intermetallics,* Vol 12 (No.7/9), Special Issue, 2004, p 957–962

53. S. Tin, L. Zhang, R.A. Hobbs, A.C. Yeh, C.M.F. Rae, and B. Broomfield, Linking the Properties, Processing, and Chemistry of Advanced Single Crystal Ni-Base Superalloys, *Proc. TMS Superalloys 2008,* 2008, p 81–90

54. Q.Z. Chen, N. Jones, and D.M. Knowles, The Macrostructures of Basc/Modified RR2072 SX Superalloys and Their Effects on Creep

Properties at Elevated Temperatures, *Acta Mater.,* Vol 50, 2002, p 1095–1112

55. H. Zhu, Y. Tang, Y. Li, Z. Hu, and C. Shi, Effect of Boron and Zirconium on Directional Solidification Behaviour and Segregation of DS IN738 Superalloy, *Mater. High Temp.,* Vol 10 (No. 1), 1992, p 39–44

56. Z. Hu, H. Song, S. Guo, and W. Sun, Role of P, S and B on Creep Behavior of Alloy 718, *J. Mater. Sci. Technol.,* Vol 17 (No. 4), 2001, p 399–402

57. M.A. Burke, J. Greggi, Jr., and G.A. Whitlow, The Effect of Boron and Carbon on the Microstructural Chemistries of Two Wrought Nickel Base Superalloys, *Scr. Metall.,* Vol 18, 1984, p 91–94

58. Y.L. Chiu and A.H.W. Ngan, Effects of Boron on the Toughness of $\gamma$-$\gamma$ Prime Nickel Aluminum Alloys, *Scr. Mater.,* Vol 40 (No. 1), 1998, p 27–32

59. U. Brill and J. Klower, High Temperature Materials, *Nickel Alloys,* U. Heubner, Ed., Marcel Dekker Inc., New York, 1998, p 129–173

60. J. Rösler and S. Müller, Protection of Ni-Base Superalloys against Stress Accelerated Grain Boundary Oxidation (SAGBO) by Grain Boundary Chemistry Modification, *Scr. Mater.,* Vol 40 (No. 2), 1999, p 257–263

61. L.R. Liu, T. Jin, N.R. Zhao, Z.H. Wang, X.F. Sun, H.R. Guan, and Z.Q. Hu, Effect of Carbon Additions on the Microstructure in a Ni-Base Single Crystal Superalloy, *Mater. Sci. Lett.,* Vol 58, 2004, p 2290–2294

62. R. Zhongci, W. Shuncai, and Z. Yunrong, Microstructure and Bonding Behavior of a New Hf-Bearing Interlayer Alloy for Single Crystal Nickel-Base Superalloy, *Scr. Mater.,* Vol 34 (No. 1), 1996, p 163–168

63. D.A. Ford, K.P.L. Fullagar, H.K. Bangu, M.C. Thomas, P.S. Burkholder, P.S. Korinko, K. Harris, and J.B. Wahl, Improved Performance Rhenium Containing Single Crystal Alloy Turbine Blades Utilizing ppm Levels of the Highly Reactive Elements Lanthanum and Yttrium, *J. Eng. Gas Turbines Power,* Vol 121 (No. 1), 1999, p 138–143

64. B. Pint, Experimental Observations in Support of the Dynamic-Segregation Theory to Explain the Reactive-Element Effect, *Oxid. Met.,* Vol 45 (No. 1–2), 1996, p 1–37

65. D. Whittle and J. Stringer, Improvement in Properties: Additives in Oxidation Resistance, *Philos. Trans. R. Soc. (London) A,* Vol 295, 1980, p 309–329

66. N. Hiramatsu and F. Stott, The Effect of Lanthanum on the Scales Developed on Thin Foils of Fe 20Cr-5Al at Very High Temperatures, *Oxid. Met.,* Vol 51 (No. 5), 1999, p 479–494

67. V. Provenzano, "The Effects of Ion Implanted Reactive Elements on the Mechanisms of Oxidation and Hot Corrosion of MCrAlY-Type Coatings," Surface Modification Technologies III, 1990

68. D. Toma, W. Brandl, and W. Koster, The Characteristics of Alumina Scales Formed on HVOF-Sprayed MCrAlY Coatings, *Oxid. Met.,* Vol 53 (No. 1/2), 2000

69. Y. Longa and M. Takemoto, The Yttrium Effect on the Corrosion Resistance of $CO_2$-Laser Processed MCrAlY Coatings, *Oxid. Met.,* Vol 41 (No. 5/6), 1994, p 301–321

70. W. Quadakkers, H. Holzbrecher, K. Briefs, and H. Beske, Differences in Growth Mechanisms of Oxide Scales Formed on ODS and Conventional Wrought Alloys, *Oxid. Met.,* Vol 32 (No. 1/2), 1989

71. R.M. Wang, Y.F. Han, C.Z. Li, S.W. Shang, D.H. Ping, and M.G. Yan, Precipitations in an Yttrium-Containing Low-Expansion Superalloy, *J. Mater. Sci.,* Vol 33, 1998, p 5069–5077

72. L. Zhao and E. Lugscheider, High Velocity Oxy-Fuel Spraying of a NiCoCrAlY and an Intermetallic NiAl-TaCr Alloy, *Surf. Coat. Technol.,* Vol 149, 2002, p 231–235

73. J.E. Gordon, *The New Science of Strong Materials, or Why You Don't Fall Through the Floor,* Pelican, 1968

74. B. Stoughton, *The Metallurgy of Iron and Steel,* McGraw-Hill, 1913

75. P.D. Merica and R.T. Waltenburg, *Trans. AIME,* Vol 71, 1925, p 709

76. X. Liu, J. Dong, B. Tang, Y. Hu, and X. Xie, Investigation of the Abnormal Effects of Phosphorous on Mechanical Properties of Inconel 718 Superalloy, *Mater. Sci. Eng. A,* Vol 270, 1999, p 190–196

77. W.D. Cao and R.L. Kennedy, Improving Stress Rupture Life of Alloy 718 by Optimizing Al, Ti, P and B Contents, *Proc. International Symposium on Superalloys and Various Derivatives,* Vol 1, 2001, p 477–488

78. M.K. Miller, J.A. Horton, W.D. Cao, and R.L. Kennedy, Characterization of the Effects of Boron and Phosphorus Additions to the Nickel-Based Superalloy 718, *J. Phys. (France) IV,* Vol 6 (No. 5), 1996, p 241–246

79. "Material Datasheets," Special Metals Corporation, 2004, http://www.specialmetals.com/products/

CHAPTER **6**

# Some Considerations in the Selection of a Superalloy

THE EFFECT OF COMPOSITION in the selection of a superalloy is briefly discussed in this chapter. Fundamental manufacturing considerations are machinability, castability, and forgeability for shaping of the part. Fundamental to the application of superalloys is their environmental resistance. The compositional considerations for both environmental resistance and manufacturing are briefly addressed.

## 6.1 Environmental Resistance

While there are several environmental-attack mechanisms that affect superalloys, such as erosion, aqueous corrosion, fretting, carburization, sulfidation, and so on, the two main mechanisms at high temperature that have the most impact on the selection of superalloy compositions are hot corrosion and oxidation.

At moderate temperatures less than approximately 870 °C (1600 °F), and with the presence of molten salts on the alloy surface, hot corrosion becomes the major mechanism of superalloy environmental attack, where the alloy material is fluxed and consumed by the corrosive species. The most effective defense mechanism against this type of corrosion is the formation of a protective chromium oxide scale, $Cr_2O_3$, which is resistant to fluxing.

At temperatures greater than approximately 950 °C (1740 °F), the main mechanism of environmental attack is oxidation. The defense mechanism is the formation of an aluminum oxide scale, $Al_2O_3$, which acts as a barrier to the diffusion of oxygen into the alloy. When sufficient aluminum and chromium are present in the alloy, the aluminum oxide layer forms rapidly and is highly adherent to the substrate. Therefore, both chromium and aluminum levels are instrumental in protecting the superalloy. Because the aluminum level in many alloys is insufficient to provide long-term protection, additional protective coatings are often applied. These coatings also prevent selective attack, which occurs along grain boundaries and at the interface between carbides and matrix, close to any exposed surface (Ref 1).

### 6.1.1 Resistance to Hot Corrosion

Generally, if hot corrosion is expected to be the principal form of environmental attack, it is desirable that the alloy should form a predominantly chromia scale, which requires high chromium levels. If type I hot corrosion temperature of 800 to 950 °C (1470 to 1740 °F) is expected, chromium levels should be 15 to 20 weight percent, while type II hot corrosion temperature of 670 to 750 °C (1240 to 1380 °F) protection requires 20 to 40 weight percent Cr. If type II hot corrosion is expected, examination of refractory levels is critical for two reasons. One is the self-sustaining hot corrosion caused by vanadium, molybdenum, and tungsten, and the other consideration is that high chromium and high levels of the refractory elements molybdenum, tungsten, and rhenium are incompatible, because the combination promotes the formation of topologically close-packed phases.

Corrosion protection also requires that carbon levels be minimized, because carbon will "sensitize" superalloys in a similar way to stainless steel, with carbon combining with chromium in grain-boundary carbide formation, leaving the alloy vulnerable to grain-boundary corrosion because the surrounding region will be chromium depleted. If stress-rupture requirements do not permit the minimization of carbon, high levels of refractory elements that form stable MC carbides, such as hafnium and zirconium, would be beneficial.

### 6.1.2 Resistance to Oxidation

If oxidation instead of hot corrosion is expected, aluminum and chromium levels should be considered together. If the weight ratio of chromium to aluminum is less than four, the alloy is an alumina former; otherwise, it is a chromia former. Generally, 5 to 10 weight percent Cr is sufficient to induce the formation of a dense alumina scale even if the aluminum level is as low as 10 atomic percent.

The next consideration is the presence of elements that may disrupt the oxide scale. Rhenium is reported to form volatile oxides at temperatures above 1000 °C (1830 °F), but one of the worst elements with respect to disrupting the alumina oxide scale is titanium, which can rapidly form a nonadherent oxide. Thus, if a precipitation-hardened alloy is being considered, one with a high aluminum/titanium ratio should be selected. If the service temperature is not too high, an alloy that forms both $\gamma''$ and $\gamma'$ can be considered, which will provide strengthening at low to intermediate temperatures. Any composition that includes reactive elements such as yttrium, cerium, or lanthanum is desirable, because the reactive-element effect will improve the adherence of the oxide scale without adversely affecting mechanical properties. Hafnium can improve both oxide scale adherence and mechanical properties.

## 6.2 Machinability

Superalloys are difficult to machine because of their intermetallic content, tendency to retain hardness at high temperatures, carbide concentration, and ease of work hardening. They are classed as having poor machinability. For precipitation-hardened alloys, the part should be machined in the annealed condition where possible. For conventional machining, tungsten carbide tools are most commonly used, although some softer alloys or alloys in an annealed state may be machined with difficulty using high-speed steel. Cubic boron nitride tools are commonly used for the harder alloys. The anisotropy of single-crystal alloys can complicate machining, because the shear stress will be very high along certain crystallographic directions.

If machining of the alloy is necessary, alloys with high carbon contents complicate the process, because carbides may form regardless of heat treatment and will reduce machinability. High boron and borides should be avoided for the same reason.

The work-hardening tendency of an alloy is typically quantified by the strain-hardening exponent ($n$) in the Holloman equation for true stress ($\sigma_t$) versus true strain ($\varepsilon_t$):

$$\sigma_t = K\varepsilon_t^n \tag{Eq 6.1}$$

where $K$ is a strength coefficient. A study on alloy 718 demonstrates that its work-hardening behavior is complex and that the Holloman relation is relatively poorly obeyed. However, in its peak aged heat treatment condition, it reasonably well follows a modified Holloman true stress versus true strain relationship known as Ludwig's equation ($\sigma_t = \sigma_0 + K\varepsilon_t^n$) and has a value of $n$ of approximately 0.72 at room temperature (Ref 2). By comparison, type 304 stainless steel, which is also known to work harden significantly during machining, has a value of $n$ (in the Holloman equation) of approximately 0.44. Low-carbon mild steel has an $n$ value of approximately 0.21 (Ref 3).

## 6.3 Forging

If forging is necessary to achieve higher toughness, the aluminum and titanium ratios should be examined carefully. If the aluminum + titanium contents are greater than six percent, it is likely that the alloy will be difficult, if not impossible, to forge, because these are the $\gamma'$ constituents (Ref 4). High $\gamma'$ volume fractions make forging difficult. Forging requires heating to above the $\gamma'$ solvus. For high $\gamma'$ fractions, the solvus temperature becomes close to the incipient melting temperature, which is a severe challenge for forging.

A low aluminum/titanium ratio is desirable because the presence of aluminum reduces ductility, while titanium is known to improve hot workability. Carbon should be minimized, because carbon will reduce the melting point at the grain boundaries and reduce the temperature at which hot forging can be carried out. Trace levels of boron have been shown to improve hot workability, because boron reduces $M_{23}C_6$ carbide agglomeration, impairs the transformation from $\gamma'$ to $\eta$, and acts as a grain refiner due to its tendency to segregate to the grain boundaries. However, boron concentrations in excess of approximately 50 ppm can be deleterious, because it causes low-melting-point borides to form at the grain boundaries.

Elimination of oxides and nitrides improves forgeability. The use of either vacuum induction or vacuum arc melting is essential for eliminating trace gases.

## 6.4 Casting

Casting is the most desirable shaping process for maximizing strength through higher $\gamma'$ volume fractions and carbide concentrations, because it allows higher concentrations of the $\gamma'$ formers aluminum and titanium, as well as of carbon, than can be present in wrought alloys. Aluminum and titanium are readily oxidized in the melt, so if high levels of these elements are present in an alloy, vacuum induction melting (VIM) must be used. Casting alloys generally require a high fluidity, which can be improved strongly through the addition of silicon (at the expense of ductility) and mildly by aluminum.

One of the most common additives in a cast alloy is hafnium, which improves ductility, thus reducing hot tearing during solidification. Tantalum also reduces hot tearing, whereas high levels of chromium increase hot tearing. The main drawback to adding hafnium is that it is a very reactive element that attacks mold materials and furnace linings, leading to the formation of brittle inclusions. Hafnium also lowers the incipient melting temperature, making solutionizing treatments more difficult and limiting the high-temperature capability of the alloy.

Hot tearing is also related to the combined zirconium plus boron content. A high content of one element greater than 250 ppm with the other element present in moderate concentrations of approximately 100 ppm contributes significantly to hot tearing, but either element individually leaves hot tearing unaffected up to levels of approximately 500 ppm. Because zirconium was primarily used as a getter of sulfur, its presence in modern cast superalloys prepared by VIM should not be required. Boron is a grain-boundary carbide former and as such tends to reduce casting porosity.

Yttrium additions are common in superalloys and very beneficial, but like hafnium, yttrium is a very reactive metal. Losses because of reaction with the ceramic furnace linings and mold material can be high, which makes compositional control of yttrium in the final cast product challenging. Lanthanum has similar benefits to yttrium but is less reactive and therefore better retained in the cast product. When added with yttrium, lanthanum tends to improve the retention of both elements.

In general, casting produces a larger grain size than forging but low pouring temperature, rapid chill casting techniques can achieve grain sizes comparable to those of forgings. Casting also allows for controlled grain alignment with directionally solidified techniques that can significantly enhance high-temperature strength and creep response when the load and longitudinal grain axis align.

With single-crystal alloys, the compositional range is narrow and very particular for each application. Originally engineered out of single-crystal alloys, the grain-boundary strengtheners boron and carbon have recently been shown to improve the tolerance to, and to reduce the number of, such defects as small "spurious grains" or very low-angle grain boundaries, which obviously degrade the perfection of the single crystal (Ref 5, 6). Hafnium has also been shown to reduce the sensitivity of the casting to defects and is added to the single-crystal alloys CMSX-186 and CMSX-486 for that purpose (Ref 5).

## REFERENCES

1. P. Kumar, The Role of Niobium and Tantalum in Superalloys, *Advances in High Temperature Structural Materials and Protective Coatings,* A.K. Koul, Ed., National Research Council of Canada, Ottawa, 1994, p 34–53
2. K.V.U. Praveen, G.V.S. Sastry, and V. Singh, Work Hardening Behavior of the Ni-Fe Based Superalloy IN718, *Metall. Mater. Trans. A,* Vol 39, 2008, p 65–78
3. W.D. Callister, *Materials Science and Engineering: An Introduction,* John Wiley & Sons, 2003, p 1–820
4. M.J. Donachie and S.J. Donachie, *Superalloys: A Technical Guide,* 2nd ed., ASM International, 2002
5. I.G. Wright and T.B. Gibbons, Recent Developments in Gas Turbine Materials and Technology and Their Implications for Syngas Firing, *Int. J. Hydrogen Energy,* Vol 32, 2007, p 3610–3621
6. E.R. Cutler, A.J. Wasson, and G.E. Fuchs, Effect of Minor Alloying Additions on the Carbide Morphology in a Single Crystal Ni-Base Superalloy, *Scr. Mater.,* Vol 58, 2008, p 146–149

APPENDIX

# Selected Superalloy Compositions

Compositions compiled from Ref 1 to 16.

## REFERENCES

1. R.J. Quigg, Tantalum's Effect on Nickel-Base Superalloys, *Proc. International Symposium on Tantalum and Niobium,* Nov 1988, p 619–629
2. Energy Conversion, Vol 18, *Encyclopedia Britannica,* 15th ed., 2002, p 332–413
3. R.T. Holt and W. Wallace, Impurities and Trace Elements in Nickel-Base Superalloys, *Int. Met. Rev.,* Vol 21, 1976, p 1–14
4. J.M. Poole, J.J. Fischer, G.A.J. Hack, and G.M. McColvin, The Development, Performance and Future of the Mechanical Alloying Process and Oxide Dispersion Strengthened Alloys, *Advances in High Temperature Structural Materials and Protective Coatings,* A.K. Koul, Ed., National Research Council of Canada, Ottawa, 1994, p 34–53
5. *Properties and Selection: Nonferrous Alloys and Pure Metals,* Vol 2, *Metals Handbook,* 9th ed., American Society for Metals, 1979, p 1–155
6. W.D. Callister, *Materials Science and Engineering: An Introduction,* John Wiley & Sons, 2003, p 1–820
7. M. Durand-Charre, *The Microstructure of Superalloys,* Gordon and Breach Science Publishers, Amsterdam, 1997, p 1–124
8. J.A. Manriquez, P.L. Bretz, L. Rabenberg, and J.K. Tien, The High Temperature Stability of IN718 Derivative Alloys, *Superalloys 1992,* S.D. Antolovich et al., Ed., TMS, 1992, p 507–516

9. K.A. Heck and J.S. Smith, Inconel Alloy 783: An Oxidation-Resistant, Low Expansion Superalloy for Gas Turbine Applications, *J. Eng. Gas Turbines Power,* Vol 120 (No. 2), 1998, p 363

10. K.A. Heck, D.F. Smith, M.A. Holderby, and J.S. Smith, Three-Phase Controlled Expansion Superalloys with Oxidation Resistance, *Superalloys 1992,* S.D. Antolovich et al., Ed., TMS, 1992, p 217–226

11. J. Davis, *Nickel, Cobalt, and Their Alloys, ASM Specialty Handbook,* ASM International, 2000

12. Y. Murata, K. Suga, and N. Yukawa, Effects of Transition Elements on the Properties of MCrAlY Carbides in IN-100 Nickel-Based Superalloy, *J. Mater. Sci.,* Vol 21 (No. 10), 1986, p 3653–3660

13. H. Murphy, C. Sims, and A. Beltran, PHACOMP Revisited, *Superalloys 1968,* M. Donachie, Ed., TMS, 1968, p 47–66; e-book, www.tms.org

14. I. Allam, D. Whittle, and J. Stringer, The Oxidation Behavior of CoCrAl Systems Containing Active Element Additions, *Oxid. Met.,* Vol 12 (No. 1), 1978, p 35–67

15. M. Thuvander and K. Stiller, Microstructure of a Boron Containing High Purity Nickel-Based Alloy 690, *Mater. Sci. Eng. A,* Vol 281, 2000, p 96–103

16. M.B. Henderson, D. Arrell, M. Heobel, R. Larsson, and G. Marchant, "Nickel-Based Superalloy Welding Practices for Industrial Gas Turbine Applications," University of Cambridge, 2002, p 1–14; http://www.msm.cam.ac.uk/phase-trans/2002/papers/APNickel Weldv2.pdf

# Cobalt Wrought Alloys

## Table A.1A  Selected cobalt wrought superalloy compositions

| Alloy | Composition, wt% | | | | | | | | | | | | | | | |
|---|---|---|---|---|---|---|---|---|---|---|---|---|---|---|---|---|
| | Fe | Co | Ni | Al | Ti | Cr | Mo | W | Nb | Ta | C | Zr | Y | La | Be | Mn |
| AiResist 213 | 0.5 | 64 | 0.5 | 3.5 | ... | 20 | ... | 4.5 | ... | 6.5 | 0.2 | 0.1 | 0.1 | ... | ... | ... |
| Elgiloy | bal. | 40 | 15 | ... | ... | 20 | 7 | ... | ... | ... | 0.15 | ... | ... | ... | .04 | 2 |
| Haynes 188(a) | 3(b) | 37 | 22 | ... | ... | 22 | ... | 15 | ... | ... | 0.1 | ... | ... | 0.9 | ... | ... |
| Haynes 25 (L-605)(a) | 3 | 50 | 10 | ... | ... | 20 | ... | 15 | ... | ... | 0.1 | ... | ... | ... | ... | 1.5 |
| K 42 B | 13 | 22 | 43 | 0.2 | 2.1 | 18 | ... | ... | ... | ... | 0.05 | ... | ... | ... | ... | ... |
| MAR-M 918(a) | ... | 52 | 20 | ... | ... | 20 | ... | ... | ... | 7.5 | 0.05 | 0.1 | ... | ... | ... | ... |
| MP159(a) | 9 | 36 | 25 | 0.2 | 3 | 19 | 7 | ... | 0.6 | ... | ... | ... | ... | ... | ... | ... |
| MP35N(a) | ... | 35 | 35 | ... | ... | 20 | 10 | ... | ... | ... | ... | ... | ... | ... | ... | ... |
| S-816(a) | 4 | 42 | 20 | ... | ... | 20 | 4 | 4 | 4 | ... | 0.38 | ... | ... | ... | ... | ... |
| Stellite B(a) | 1 | 61.5 | 1 | ... | ... | 30 | ... | 4.5 | ... | ... | 1 | ... | ... | ... | ... | ... |
| UMCo-50(a) | 21 | 49 | ... | ... | ... | 28 | ... | ... | ... | ... | 0.12 | ... | ... | ... | ... | ... |

(a) Strengthening mechanism, solid-solution hardened (SSH). (b) Maximum element concentration. Source: Ref 1–16

## Table A.1B  Applications and comments to selected superalloys in Table A.1A

| Alloy | Application | Comments |
|---|---|---|
| AiResist 213 | Sheets, tubing | ... |
| Elgiloy | Springs | High strength and corrosion resistance |
| Haynes 188 | GTE combustors, flame holders, liners and transition ducts | High temperature strength and oxidation resistance up to 1093 °C (2000 °F). Cr + La produce tenacious oxide scale. High sulfidation resistance and metallurgical stability to high temperature exposure. Good formability and weldability |
| Haynes 25 (L-605) | GTE combustor liners and other low load components, industrial furnace muffles/liners in high temperature kilns | Good formability and high strength up to 816 °C (1500 °F) and oxidation resistance up to 1093 °C (2000 °F). Good sulfidation resistance and resistance to wear and galling. Moderate strength and high oxidation resistance applications. |
| MAR-M 918 | High-temperature sheets | ... |
| MP159 | Hot corrosion resistant, high-strength fasteners | ... |
| MP35N | Fasteners, springs, nonmagnetic electrical components and instrument parts in medical, seawater, oil and gas wells, and chemical and food processing environments | Excellent resistance to sulfidation, high temperature oxidation, hydrogen embrittlement, saline solutions and most mineral acids. Also resistant to pitting and crevice corrosion. Tensile strength of 2068 MPa (300 ksi) at low temperatures (SSH + work + PH); where SSH = solid-solution hardened, PH = precipitation hardened; service temperatures up to 400 °C (750 °F). |

Source: Ref 1–16

# Cobalt Cast Alloys

**Table A.2A  Selected cobalt cast superalloy compositions**

| Alloy | Fe | Co | Ni | Al | Ti | Cr | Mo | W | Nb | Ta | Re | B | C | Zr | Y | Si | Mn |
|---|---|---|---|---|---|---|---|---|---|---|---|---|---|---|---|---|---|
| | | | | | | | | Composition wt% | | | | | | | | | |
| AiResist 215 | 0.5 | 63 | 0.5 | 4.3 | ... | 19 | ... | 4.5 | ... | 7.5 | ... | ... | 0.35 | 0.1 | 0.1 | ... | ... |
| FSX-414 | 1 | 52.5 | 10 | ... | ... | 29 | ... | 7.5 | ... | ... | ... | 0.01 | 0.25 | ... | ... | ... | ... |
| FSX-418 | 2(c) | bal. | 11 | ... | ... | 29.5 | ... | 7 | ... | ... | ... | 0.012 | 0.25 | ... | 0.2 | 1(c) | 1(c) |
| FSX-430 | ... | bal. | 10 | ... | ... | 29.5 | ... | 7.5 | ... | ... | ... | 0.027 | 0.4 | 0.9 | 0.5 | ... | ... |
| Haynes 21 | 1 | 64 | 3 | ... | ... | 27 | 5 | ... | ... | ... | ... | ... | 0.25 | ... | ... | ... | ... |
| Haynes 25 (L-605) | 1 | 54 | 10 | ... | ... | 20 | ... | 15 | ... | ... | ... | ... | 0.1 | ... | ... | ... | ... |
| Jetalloy 1570(a) | 2 | 46 | 28 | ... | 4 | 20 | ... | ... | ... | ... | ... | ... | 0.2 | ... | ... | ... | ... |
| Jetalloy 1650(a) | ... | 36 | 27 | ... | 3.8 | 19 | ... | 12 | ... | 2 | ... | 0.02 | 0.2 | 0.2 | ... | ... | ... |
| MAR-M 302 | 0.5 | 58 | ... | ... | ... | 21.5 | ... | 10 | ... | 9 | ... | 0.005 | 0.85 | 0.2 | ... | ... | ... |
| MAR-M 322 | 0.5 | 60.5 | ... | ... | 0.75 | 21.5 | ... | 9 | ... | 4.5 | ... | ... | 1 | 2 | ... | ... | ... |
| MAR-M 509 | ... | 54.5 | 10 | ... | 0.2 | 23.5 | ... | 7 | ... | 3.5 | ... | ... | 0.6 | 0.5 | ... | ... | ... |
| NASA Co-W-Re | ... | 67.5 | ... | ... | 1 | 3 | ... | 25 | ... | ... | 2 | ... | 0.4 | ... | ... | ... | ... |
| S-816(b) | 4 | 42 | 20 | ... | ... | 20 | 4 | 4 | 4 | ... | ... | ... | 0.4 | ... | ... | 0.4 | 1.2 |
| V-36 | 3 | 42 | 20 | ... | ... | 25 | 4 | 2 | 2 | ... | ... | ... | 0.27 | ... | ... | 0.4 | 1 |
| WI-52 | 2 | 63.5 | ... | ... | ... | 21 | ... | 11 | 2 (Nb+Ta) | ... | ... | ... | 0.45 | ... | ... | ... | ... |
| X-40 (Stellite alloy 31) | 1.5 | 57.5 | 10 | ... | ... | 22 | ... | 7.5 | ... | ... | ... | ... | 0.5 | ... | ... | 0.5 | 0.5 |
| X-45 | 2(c) | bal. | 11 | ... | ... | 25.5 | ... | 7 | ... | ... | ... | 0.01 | 0.25 | ... | ... | ... | 1(c) |

Strengthening mechanism (a) precipitation hardened (PH), (b) solid-solution hardened (SSH). (c) Maximum element concentration. Source: Ref 1–16

**Table A.2B  Applications and comments to selected superalloys in Table A.2A**

| Alloy | Application | Comments |
|---|---|---|
| AiResist 215 | Gas turbine engine, (GTE) stator vanes | Resistant to hot corrosion |
| FSX-414 | GTE stator vanes | |
| FSX-418 | GTE stator vanes | GTE stator vanesImproved oxidation resistance over FSX-414 |
| FSX-430 | GTE stator vanes | |
| Haynes 21 | ... | Improved strength and ductility |
| MAR-M 302 | GTE blades, vanes | Modified Vitallium with improved stress-rupture |
| MAR-M 322 | GTE blades, vanes | ... |
| MAR-M 509 | GTE blades, vanes | ... |
| NASA Co-W-Re | High-temperature space applications | ... |
| S-816 | GTE blades, bolts, springs | ... |
| WI-52 | GTE stator vanes, parts | ... |
| X-40 (Stellite alloy 31) | GTE stator vanes, parts | ... |
| X-45 | GTE stator vanes | ... |

Source: Ref 1–16

# Iron Wrought and Powder Metallurgy Alloys

**Table A.3A  Selected iron wrought and powder metallurgy superalloy compositions**

| Alloy | Fe | Co | Ni | Al | Ti | Cr | Mo | W | Nb | Ta | B | C | Zr | La | $Y_2O_3$ | Si | Mn | Cu | V | N |
|---|---|---|---|---|---|---|---|---|---|---|---|---|---|---|---|---|---|---|---|---|
| 19-9DL(a) | 66.8 | ... | 9 | ... | 0.3 | 19 | 1.3 | 1.3 | 0.4 | ... | ... | 0.3 | ... | ... | ... | 0.6 | 1.1 | ... | ... | ... |
| A-286(b) | 55.2 | ... | 26 | 0.2 | 2 | 15 | 1.3 | ... | ... | ... | 0.005 | 0.04 | ... | ... | ... | ... | ... | ... | 0.3 | ... |
| D-979(b) | bal. | ... | 45 | 1 | 3 | 15 | 4 | 4 | ... | ... | 0.01 | 0.05 | ... | ... | ... | 0.75(e) | 0.75(e) | ... | ... | ... |
| Discaloy(b) | 55 | ... | 26 | 0.25 | 1.7 | 14 | 3 | ... | ... | ... | ... | 0.06 | ... | ... | ... | ... | ... | ... | ... | ... |
| Hastelloy X(a) | 15.8 | 1.5(e) | 49 | 2 | ... | 22 | 9 | 0.6 | ... | ... | ... | 0.15 | ... | ... | ... | ... | ... | ... | ... | ... |
| Haynes 556(a) | 29 | 20 | 21 | 0.3 | ... | 22 | 3 | 2.5 | 0.1 | 0.5 | ... | 0.1 | 0.002 | 0.02 | ... | ... | ... | ... | ... | ... |
| 19-9DL(a) | 66.8 | ... | 9 | ... | 0.3 | 19 | 1.3 | 1.3 | 0.4 | ... | ... | 0.3 | ... | ... | ... | 0.6 | 1.1 | ... | ... | ... |
| Incoloy 800(a) | 45.7 | ... | 33 | 0.15–0.6 | 0.15–0.6 | 21 | ... | ... | ... | ... | ... | 0.1(e) | ... | ... | ... | ... | ... | ... | ... | ... |
| Incoloy 800H(a) | 45.8 | ... | 33 | 0.15–0.6 | 0.15–0.6 | 21 | ... | ... | ... | ... | ... | 0.05–0.1 | ... | ... | ... | ... | ... | ... | ... | ... |
| Incoloy 800HT(a) | 46 | ... | 33 | 0.25–0.6 | 0.25–0.6 | 21 | ... | ... | ... | ... | ... | 0.06–0.1 | ... | ... | ... | 0.5 | 0.8 | 0.4 | ... | ... |
| Incoloy 801(a) | 46.3 | ... | 32 | ... | 1.13 | 20.5 | ... | ... | ... | ... | ... | 0.05 | ... | ... | ... | ... | ... | ... | ... | ... |
| Incoloy 802(a) | 44.8 | ... | 33 | 0.58 | 0.75 | 21 | ... | ... | ... | ... | ... | 0.35 | ... | ... | ... | ... | ... | ... | ... | ... |
| Incoloy 901(b) | 36.2 | ... | 43 | ... | 2.7 | 12.5 | 6 | ... | ... | ... | ... | 0.10(e) | ... | ... | ... | ... | ... | ... | ... | ... |
| Incoloy 903(b) | 41 | 15 | 38 | 0.7 | 1.4 | 0.1(e) | 0.1 | ... | 3 | ... | ... | 0.04 | ... | ... | ... | ... | ... | ... | ... | ... |
| Incoloy 907(b) | 42 | 13 | 38 | 0.03 | 1.5 | ... | ... | ... | 4.7 | ... | ... | 0.01 | ... | ... | ... | 0.15 | ... | ... | ... | ... |
| Incoloy 909(b) | 42 | 13 | 38 | 0.03 | 1.5 | ... | ... | ... | 4.7 | ... | ... | 0.01 | ... | ... | ... | 0.4 | ... | ... | ... | ... |
| Incoloy 925(b) | 29 | ... | 44 | 0.2 | 2.1 | 20.5 | 2.8 | ... | ... | ... | ... | 0.01 | ... | ... | ... | 0.05 | ... | 1.8 | ... | ... |
| Inconel 706(b) | bal. | ... | 42 | 0.2 | 1.8 | 16 | ... | ... | 2.9 | ... | 0.03 | 0.01 | ... | ... | ... | ... | ... | ... | ... | ... |
| Inconel 718(b) | 18.5 | ... | 53 | 0.5 | 0.9 | 19 | 3 | ... | 5.1 | ... | ... | 0.08(e) | ... | ... | ... | ... | ... | 0.15(e) | ... | ... |
| Inconel 783(b) | bal. | 34 | 29 | 5.4 | 0.1 | 3 | ... | ... | 3 | ... | ... | ... | ... | ... | ... | ... | ... | ... | ... | ... |
| N-155 (Multimet)(a) | 32.2 | 20 | 20 | ... | ... | 21 | 3 | 2.5 | 1 | ... | ... | 0.15 | 0.02 | 0.2 | ... | ... | ... | ... | ... | 0.2 |
| Pyromet CTX-1(b) | 39 | 16 | 38 | 1 | 1.7 | 0.1(e) | 0.1 | ... | 3 | ... | ... | 0.03 | ... | ... | ... | ... | ... | ... | ... | ... |
| REX-78(a) | 60 | 18 | 18 | 0.6 | 0.6 | 14 | 4 | ... | ... | ... | 0.015 | 0.01 | ... | ... | ... | ... | ... | 4 | ... | ... |
| Thermo-Span(b) | 34.5 | 29 | 25 | 0.45 | 0.85 | 5.5 | ... | ... | 4.8 | ... | 0.004 | 0.08(e) | ... | ... | ... | 0.35 | ... | ... | 0.5(e) | ... |
| V-57(b) | 48.6 | ... | 27 | 0.25 | 3 | 14.8 | 1.3 | ... | ... | ... | 0.01 | 0.08(e) | ... | ... | ... | ... | ... | ... | ... | ... |
| W-545(b) | 55.8 | ... | 26 | 0.2 | 2.85 | 13.5 | 1.5 | ... | ... | ... | 0.05 | 0.08(e) | ... | ... | ... | ... | ... | ... | ... | ... |
| MA-956(c)(d) | bal. | ... | ... | 4.5 | 0.5 | 20 | ... | ... | ... | ... | ... | 0.05 | ... | ... | 0.5 | ... | ... | ... | ... | ... |

Strengthening mechanism (a) solid-solution hardened (SSH), (b) precipitation hardened (PH), (c) oxide dispersion strengthened (ODS), (d) Powder metallurgy. (e) Maximum element concentration. Source: Ref 1–16

**Table A.3B  Applications and comments to selected superalloys in Table A.3A**

| Alloy | Application | Comments |
|---|---|---|
| 19-9DL | Turbine and super-charger wheels, industrial gas turbine blades, casings, afterburner components | Low cost. High strength, corrosion, and oxidation resistance up to 677 °C (1250 °F) |
| A-286 | GTE blades, vanes, shafts, tail cones, afterburners, springs and fasteners, automotive components | Good strength and oxidation resistance up to 700 °C (1290 °F). Good fabrication characteristics |
| D-979 | ... | Designed for strength between 649–760 °C (1200–1400 °F). Hardened by complex intermetallic precipitation. Corrosion resistant and high tensile and stress-rupture strengths |
| Discaloy | GTE parts, bolts | ... |
| Hastelloy X | GTE combustors and fabricated parts | Good strength, oxidation resistance, and fabricability |
| Haynes 556 | GTE sheet components (combustors, transition ducts, afterburners), waste incineration, heat treating, calcining, chemical processing, galvanizing, refinery and boiler applications, filler metal for welding dissimilar metals (Fe-Co) | Similar to N-155 with improved composition control. Improved oxidation and hot corrosion resistance, weldability and high-temperature ductility, and higher thermal shock and fatigue resistance |
| Incoloy 800 | Process piping, heat exchangers, carburizing equipment, heating-element sheathing, nuclear steam-generator tubing | Good strength and excellent oxidation and carburization resistance |
| Incoloy 800H | Chemical and petrochemical processing, super-heater and reheater tubing in power plants, industrial furnaces, heat treating equipment | Based on IN-800. Closer control of C contents and different heat treatment result in higher creep strength |
| Incoloy 800HT | Chemical and petrochemical processing, super-heater and reheater tubing in power plants, industrial furnaces, heat treating equipment | Based on IN-800. Closer control of C, Al+Ti (0.3–1.2) contents and different heat treatment result in higher creep strength |
| Incoloy 801 | Petroleum hydrotreaters, heat exchangers | ... |
| Incoloy 802 | Heat exchanger and condenser tubing | Stress-corrosion cracking resistant |
| Incoloy 901 | GTE rotors, parts | ... |
| Incoloy 903 | GTE rings and casings, rocket components | Low and constant coefficient of thermal expansion (CTE) up to 430 °C (805 °F). Highly thermal fatigue and shock resistant (may be related to its constant Young's modulus) |
| Incoloy 907 | GTE seals, shafts, and casings | Low CTE. Improved notch-rupture properties at elevated temperatures to IN-903 |
| Incoloy 909 | GTE casings, shrouds, vanes, and shafts | Low CTE. Silicon addition improves notch-rupture and tensile properties with less restrictive processing and shorter heat treatments |
| Incoloy 925 | Surface and down-hole hardware in sour gas wells, oil-production equipment | Excellent resistance to general corrosion, and stress-corrosion cracking in many aqueous environments, including those containing sulfides and chlorides, combined with high strength |
| Inconel 706 | ... | Representative of wrought Ni alloys for industrial gas turbine applications. Derived from 718 |
| Inconel 718 | Used for turbine wheels, shafts, supports, and other components | Most widely used of all wrought superalloys. Creep-rupture strength up to 700 °C (1290 °F) |
| Inconel 783 | Rings, casings, shrouds, and seals for GTE compressors, turbines, and exhaust systems | Relatively low CTE and high stress-assisted grain-boundary oxidation resistance. Hardened by three-phase precipitation |
| N-155 (Multimet) | GTE sheet, parts (combustors, transition ducts, afterburners). Furnace hardware and industrial fans | Predecessor of Haynes 556. Extensively used in older aircraft GTEs. High-stress applications up to 820 °C (1510 °F) and moderate-stress applications up to 1090 °C (1995 °F) |
| REX-78 | ... | Used for blading in Whittle engine |
| V-57 | GTE rotors | ... |
| W-545 | GTE parts, bolts | ... |
| MA-956 | GTE combustion chambers, energy-conversion systems | Ferritic-matrix ODS alloy. Exceptional strength and resistance to oxidation, carburization, and hot corrosion at temperatures above 1100 °C (2010 °F) |

Source: Ref 1-16

# Nickel Cast Alloys

Table A.4A  Selected nickel cast superalloy compositions

Composition, wt%

| Alloy | Fe | Co | Ni | Al | Ti | Cr | Mo | W | Nb | Ta | Re | Ru | B | C | Zr | Hf | La | Si | Mn | Cu | V |
|---|---|---|---|---|---|---|---|---|---|---|---|---|---|---|---|---|---|---|---|---|---|
| AM-1(a)(b) | ... | 6.5 | 64 | 5.2 | 1.1 | 7.8 | 2 | 5.7 | ... | 7.9 | ... | ... | ... | ... | ... | ... | ... | ... | ... | ... | ... |
| AM-3(a)(b) | 0.1 | 5.5 | 68 | 6 | 2 | 8 | 2.3 | 5 | ... | 3.5 | ... | ... | ... | 0.007 | ... | ... | ... | ... | ... | ... | ... |
| B-1900(a) | ... | 10 | 64 | 6 | 1 | 8 | 6 | ... | ... | ... | ... | ... | 0.015 | ... | 0.1 | ... | 4 | ... | ... | ... | ... |
| B-1900 + Hf(a) | 0.1 | 10 | 64 | 6 | 1 | 8 | 6 | ... | ... | ... | ... | ... | 0.015 | ... | 0.1 | 1.5 | 4 | ... | ... | ... | ... |
| C-1023(a) | ... | 10 | 58 | 4.2 | 3.6 | 15.5 | 8.5 | ... | ... | ... | ... | ... | 0.006 | 0.16 | ... | ... | ... | ... | ... | ... | ... |
| CM-186LC(a)(c) | ... | 9.3 | bal. | 5.7 | 0.7 | 6 | 0.5 | 8.4 | ... | 3.4 | 3 | ... | 0.015 | 0.07 | 0.005 | 1.4 | ... | ... | ... | ... | ... |
| CM-247LC(a)(c) | ... | 9.3 | bal. | 5.6 | 0.7 | 8 | 0.5 | 9.5 | ... | 3.2 | ... | ... | 0.015 | 0.07 | 0.01 | 1.4 | ... | ... | ... | ... | ... |
| CMSX-10(a)(b) | ... | 1.5–9.0 | bal. | 5.0–7.0 | 0.1–1.2 | 1.8–4.0 | 0.25–2.0 | ... | ... | 7.0–10. | ... | ... | ... | ... | 3.5–7.5 | ... | ... | ... | ... | ... | ... |
| CMSX-11B(a)(b) | ... | 7 | 62 | 3.6 | 4.2 | 12.5 | 0.5 | 5 | 0.1 | 5 | ... | ... | ... | ... | 0.04 | ... | ... | ... | ... | ... | ... |
| CMSX-11C(a)(b) | ... | 3 | 65 | 3.4 | 4.2 | 14.9 | 0.4 | 4.5 | 0.1 | 5 | ... | ... | ... | ... | 0.04 | ... | ... | ... | ... | ... | ... |
| CMSX-2(a)(b) | ... | 4.6 | 66 | 5.6 | 1 | 8 | 0.6 | 8 | ... | 6 | ... | ... | ... | ... | 6 | ... | ... | ... | ... | ... | ... |
| CMSX-3(a)(b) | ... | 4.8 | bal. | 5.6 | 1 | 8 | 0.6 | 8 | ... | 6.3 | ... | ... | 0.001 | 0.003 | ... | 0.1 | ... | ... | ... | ... | ... |
| CMSX-4(a)(b) | ... | 9 | bal. | 5.6 | ... | 6.5 | 0.6 | 6 | ... | 6.5 | 2.9 | ... | ... | ... | ... | 0.1 | ... | ... | ... | ... | ... |
| CMSX-486(a)(b) | ... | 9.3 | bal. | 5.7 | 0.1 | 5 | 0.5 | 8.4 | ... | 6 | 3 | ... | 0.015 | 0.09 | 0.005 | 1.4 | ... | ... | ... | ... | ... |
| CMSX-6(a)(b) | ... | 5 | bal. | 4.8 | 4.7 | 10 | 3 | ... | ... | 2 | ... | ... | ... | ... | ... | ... | ... | ... | ... | ... | ... |
| CMSX-681(a)(b) | ... | 9.3 | bal. | 5.7 | 0.1 | 5 | 0.5 | 8.4 | ... | 6 | 3 | ... | 0.015 | 0.09 | 0.005 | 1.4 | ... | ... | ... | ... | ... |
| Ford 406(a) | 10 | 10 | bal. | 4.5 | 2 | 6 | 1 | 8.5 | 2 | ... | ... | ... | ... | ... | ... | ... | ... | ... | ... | ... | ... |
| GMR-235(a) | 10 | 1 | 63 | 3 | 2 | 15.5 | 5.3 | 1 | ... | ... | ... | ... | 0.06 | 0.15 | ... | ... | ... | 0.6 | 0.3 | ... | ... |
| Hastelloy X(d) | 18 | 1 | 50 | ... | ... | 21 | 9 | 1 | ... | ... | ... | ... | ... | 0.1 | ... | ... | ... | ... | ... | ... | ... |
| Illium G(d) | ... | ... | bal. | ... | ... | 22 | 6 | ... | ... | ... | ... | ... | ... | 0.2 | ... | ... | ... | ... | ... | 5 | ... |
| Inconel 100(a) | ... | 15 | 61 | 5.5 | 5 | 10 | 3 | ... | ... | ... | ... | ... | 0.01 | 0.18 | 0.06 | ... | ... | ... | ... | ... | 1 |
| Inconel 690(d) | 9 | ... | 61 | ... | ... | 29 | ... | ... | ... | ... | ... | ... | ... | 0.02 | ... | ... | ... | 0.2 | 0.2 | ... | ... |
| Inconel 713 LC(a) | ... | ... | 75 | 6 | 0.6 | 12 | 4.5 | ... | ... | 4 | ... | ... | 0.01 | 0.05 | 0.1 | ... | ... | ... | ... | ... | ... |
| Inconel 713C(a) | ... | ... | 74 | 6 | 0.8 | 12.5 | 4.2 | ... | 0.9 | 1.75 | ... | ... | 0.012 | 0.12 | 0.1 | ... | ... | ... | ... | 2 | ... |
| Inconel 718(a) | 18 | ... | 53 | 0.5 | 0.9 | 19 | 3 | ... | 5 | ... | ... | ... | ... | 0.04 | ... | ... | ... | ... | ... | ... | ... |
| Inconel 738(a) | ... | 8.5 | 62 | 3.4 | 3.4 | 16 | 1.8 | 2.6 | 2 | ... | ... | ... | 0.01 | 0.17 | 0.1 | ... | ... | ... | ... | ... | ... |
| Inconel 738 LC(a) | ... | 8.5 | 61 | 3.4 | 3.4 | 16 | 1.7 | 2.6 | 0.9 | 1.7 | ... | ... | ... | 0.11 | 0.05 | ... | ... | ... | ... | ... | ... |
| Inconel 792(a) | ... | 9 | 60 | 3.2 | 4.2 | 13 | 2 | 4 | 2 | ... | ... | ... | 0.02 | 0.2 | 0.1 | ... | ... | ... | ... | 0.1 | ... |
| Inconel 792(a) | ... | 9.2 | bal. | 3.5 | 3.9 | 12.4 | 1.9 | 3.9 | ... | 4.2 | ... | ... | 0.016 | 0.07 | 0.018 | ... | ... | 0.2 | ... | ... | ... |
| Inconel 939(a) | ... | 19 | 48 | 1.9 | 3.7 | 22.5 | ... | 2 | 1 | 1.4 | ... | ... | 0.009 | 0.15 | 0.09 | ... | ... | ... | ... | ... | ... |
| Inconel 939(a) | ... | 19 | 48 | 1.9 | 3.7 | 22.5 | ... | 2 | 1 | 1.4 | ... | ... | ... | 0.15 | ... | ... | ... | ... | ... | ... | ... |
| M22(a) | ... | ... | 71 | 6.3 | ... | 5.7 | 2 | 11 | ... | 3 | ... | ... | ... | 0.13 | 0.6 | ... | ... | ... | ... | ... | ... |
| M-252(a) | ... | 10 | 56 | 1 | 2.6 | 20 | 10 | ... | ... | ... | ... | ... | 0.005 | 0.15 | ... | ... | ... | ... | ... | ... | ... |
| MAR-M 211(a) | 1 | 10 | 59 | 5 | 2 | 9 | ... | 13 | 1 | ... | ... | ... | 0.015 | 0.15 | 0.05 | 1.5 | ... | ... | ... | ... | ... |
| MAR-M 200(a) | 1 | 10 | 59 | 5 | 2 | 9 | ... | 13 | 1 | ... | ... | ... | 0.015 | 0.15 | 0.05 | ... | ... | ... | ... | ... | ... |

(continued)

Strengthening mechanism (a) precipitation hardened (PH), (b) single crystal (SX), (c) directionally solidified (DS), (d) solid-solution hardened (SSH). (e) Maximum element concentration. Source: Ref 1–16

**Table A.4A  (continued)**

Composition, wt%

| Alloy | Fe | Co | Ni | Al | Ti | Cr | Mo | W | Nb | Ta | Re | Ru | B | C | Zr | Hf | La | Si | Mn | Cu | V |
|---|---|---|---|---|---|---|---|---|---|---|---|---|---|---|---|---|---|---|---|---|---|
| MAR-M 246(a) | | 10 | 60 | 5.5 | 1.5 | 9 | 2.5 | 10 | | 1.5 | | | 0.015 | 0.15 | 0.05 | | | | | | |
| MAR-M 247(a) | 0.5 | 10 | 59 | 5.5 | 1 | 8.25 | 0.7 | 10 | | 3 | | | 0.015 | 0.15 | 0.05 | 1.5 | | | | | |
| MAR-M 421(a) | | 9.5 | 61 | 4.3 | 1.8 | 15.8 | 2 | 3.8 | 2 | | | | 0.015 | 0.14 | 0.05 | | | | | | |
| MC2(a)(b) | | 5.3 | bal. | 5 | 1.5 | 8 | 2 | 8 | | | | | | 0.01(e) | | | | | | | |
| MM-002 (RR-7080)(a) (c) | | 10 | 61 | 5.5 | 1.5 | 9 | | 10 | | 2.5 | | | 0.015 | 0.14 | 0.05 | 1.5 | | | | | |
| MM-004(a) | | | 74 | 5.9 | 0.6 | 12 | 4.5 | | 2 | | | | 0.015 | 0.05 | 0.05 | 1.3 | | | | | |
| MM-005(a) | | 10 | 59 | 4.8 | 2.5 | 8.5 | 2 | 8 | | 3.8 | | | 0.015 | 0.11 | 0.05 | 1.4 | | | | | |
| MM-006(a) | | 10 | 63 | 5.5 | 1.5 | 9 | 2.5 | 10 | | 1.5 | | | 0.015 | 0.14 | 0.05 | 1.8 | | | | | |
| MM-009(a) | | 10 | 59 | 5 | 2 | 9 | | 13 | 1 | | | | 0.015 | 0.14 | 0.05 | 1.8 | | | | | |
| MS2(a)(b) | | 5 | 65 | 5 | 1.5 | 8 | 2 | 8 | | 6 | | | | | | | | | | | |
| N-4(a)(b) | | 7.5 | bal. | 3.7 | 4.2 | 9.2 | 1.5 | 6 | 0.5 | 4 | | | | | | | | | | | |
| PWA 1480(a)(b) | | 5 | bal. | 5 | 1.5 | 10 | | 4 | | 12 | | | | | | | | | | | |
| PWA 1484(a)(b) | | 10 | bal. | 5.6 | | 5 | 2 | 6 | | 9 | | | | | | | | | | | |
| René 100(a) | | 15 | 61 | 5.5 | 4.2 | 9.5 | 3 | | | | | | 0.015 | 0.18 | 0.06 | | | | | | 1 |
| René 41(a) | | 11 | 55 | 1.5 | 3.1 | 19 | 10 | | | | | | 0.01 | 0.09 | | | | | | | |
| René 77(a) | | 15 | 58 | 4.3 | 3.3 | 15 | 4.2 | | 0.04 | | | | 0.015 | 0.07 | | | | | | | |
| René 80(a) | 3 | 9.5 | 60 | 3 | 5 | 14 | 4 | 4 | | | | | 0.015 | 0.17 | 0.03 | | | | | | |
| René 80H(a)(c) | | 9.5 | 60 | 3 | 4.8 | 14 | 4 | 4 | | | | | 0.015 | 0.08 | 0.02 | 0.75 | | | | | |
| René N4(a)(b) | | 7.5 | 62 | 4.2 | 3.5 | 9.8 | 1.5 | 6 | 0.5 | 4.8 | | | 0.004 | 0.06 | | 0.15 | | | | | |
| René N5(a)(b) | | 8 | bal. | 6.2 | | 7 | 2 | 5 | | 7 | | | | | | | | | | | |
| René N6(a)(b) | | 10–15 | bal. | 5–6.25 | | 4.25–6 | 0.5–2 | 5–6.5 | | 7–9.25 | | | | | | | | | | | |
| RR 2000(a)(b) | | 15 | bal. | 5.5 | 4 | 10 | 3 | | | | | | | | | | | | | | 1 |
| RR 2072(a)(b) | | 4 | bal. | 6.2 | 0.4 | 6 | 3.3 | 1.9 | 0.8 | 5.95 | 3 | | | | | 0.1 | | | | | |
| SEL(a) | 1(e) | 26 | 51 | 4.4 | 2.4 | 15 | | | 0.5 | | | | 0.015 | 0.08 | | | | 0.5(e) | 0.3(e) | | |
| SEL-15(a) | 0.5(e) | 14.5 | 58 | 5.4 | 2.5 | 11 | | 1.5 | 0.5 | | | | 0.015 | 0.07 | | | | 0.5(e) | 0.3(e) | | |
| SRR 99(a)(b) | | 5 | bal. | 5.5 | 2.2 | 8 | | 10 | | 3 | | | | | | | | | | | |
| TMS-82(a)(b) | | 7.8 | bal. | 5.3 | 0.5 | 4.9 | 1.9 | 8.7 | | 6.0 | 2.4 | | | | | 0.1 | | | | | |
| TRW-NASA VIA(a) | | 7.5 | 61 | 5.4 | 1 | 6.1 | 2 | 5.8 | 0.5 | 9 | 0.5 | | 0.02 | 0.13 | 0.13 | 0.4 | | | | | |
| Udimet 500(a) | 2 | 17 | 53 | 3 | 3 | 18 | 4 | | | | | | | 0.1 | | | | | | | |
| Udimet 700(a) | | 18.5 | 54 | 4.25 | 3.5 | 15 | 5.3 | | | | | | 0.03 | 0.1 | | | | | | | |
| Udimet 710(a) | | 15 | 55 | 2.5 | 5 | 18 | 3 | 1.5 | | | | | | 0.13 | 0.08 | | | | | | |
| UDM56(a) | 5 | 5 | 64 | 4.5 | 2 | 16 | 1.5 | 6 | | | | | 0.07 | 0.02 | 0.03 | | | | | | |
| UM-F13(a) | | 6.8 | 59 | 5.6 | | | 4.3 | 4.3 | | 6.3 | 3.7 | 14 | | | | | | | | | |
| Waspaloy(a) | 1 | 13.5 | 58 | 1.2 | 3 | 19.5 | 4.2 | | | | | | 0.005 | 0.07 | 0.09 | | | | | | |
| WAX-20(c) | | | 72 | 6.5 | | | | 20 | | | | | | 0.2 | 1.5 | | | | | | 0.5 |

Strengthening mechanism (a) precipitation hardened (PH), (b) single crystal (SX), (c) directionally solidified (DS), (d) solid-solution hardened (SSH), (e) Maximum element concentration. Source: Ref 1–16

**Table A.4B    Applications and comments to selected superalloys in Table A.4A**

| Alloy | Application | Comments |
|---|---|---|
| AM-3 | ... | Similar to MC2 in microstructure but not topologically close-packed prone |
| B-1900 | GTE parts | ... |
| CMSX-11B | ... | Designed to meet hot corrosion requirements of industrial turbines |
| CMSX-11C | ... | Designed to meet hot corrosion requirements of industrial turbines |
| CMSX-3 | ... | Hf added to improve aluminide coating adherence |
| CMSX-6 | ... | Low-density SX (low Ta) |
| Ford 406 | Integrally cast turbine wheels | ... |
| GMR-235 | GTE parts | ... |
| Hastelloy X | ... | Good oxidation resistance |
| Illium G | ... | Resists hot sulfuric, hydrofluoric, nitric, and phosphoric acids |
| Inconel 100 | GTE blades and wheels | ... |
| Inconel 713 LC | GTE blades, parts | ... |
| Inconel 713C | GTE blades, parts | ... |
| Inconel 738 | ... | Developed to increase hot corrosion resistance without strength loss |
| Inconel 792 | ... | Developed to increase corrosion resistance without strength loss. Available as PC, DS, and SX(a) |
| Inconel 792 | Turbine blades | Inconel 792 with tantalum. Good hot corrosion resistance |
| MAR-M 211 | Integrally cast turbine wheels, blades | MAR-M 200 + Hf. Also available in SX form (PWA 1422) |
| MAR-M 200 | GTE blades | ... |
| MAR-M 246 | GTE blades | Better ductility than MAR-M 200 |
| MAR-M 247 | ... | Extremely difficult to weld |
| MAR-M 421 | ... | Superior hot corrosion resistance and stability |
| MM-002 (RR-7080) | GTE parts | Hf modified for improved ductility |
| MM-004 | GTE parts | IN-713 + Hf. Improved ductility |
| MM-005 | ... | René 125 + Hf |
| MM-006 | ... | MAR-M 246 + Hf |
| MM-009 | ... | MAR-M 200 + Hf |
| N-4 | ... | Based on René 80 |
| PWA 1480 | ... | First commercial SX(a) superalloy |
| René 77 | GTE parts | Phase controlled to be sigma free after long-time exposure |
| René 80 | Turbine blade alloy | ... |
| René 80H | ... | Hf addition to improve ductility during casting and reduce crack formation |
| SEL | High-temperature parts | ... |
| SEL -15 | High-strength parts | ... |
| TRW-NASA VIA | Turbine blade alloy | ... |

(a) Polycrystalline (PC), directionally solidified (DS), single crystal (SX).   Source: Ref 1–16

# Nickel Wrought Alloys

**Table A.5A   Selected nickel wrought superalloy compositions**

| Alloy | Fe | Co | Ni | Al | Ti | Cr | Mo | W | Nb | Ta | B | C | Zr | Hf | Y | La | Si | Mn | Mg | Cu | V |
|---|---|---|---|---|---|---|---|---|---|---|---|---|---|---|---|---|---|---|---|---|---|
| Astroloy(a) | 0.3(c) | 15 | 57 | 4.4 | 3.5 | 15 | 5.3 | … | … | … | 0.03 | 0.06 | 0.06 | … | … | … | … | … | … | … | … |
| C-263(a) | 0.7(c) | 20 | 51 | 0.45 | 2.1 | 20 | 5.9 | … | … | … | … | 0.06 | … | … | … | … | … | … | … | … | … |
| Custom Age 625 Plus(a) | 5 | … | 61 | 0.2 | 1.3 | 21 | 8 | … | 3.4 | … | … | 0.01 | … | … | … | … | … | … | … | … | 0.03 |
| Hastelloy B(b) | 5 | 2.5(c) | 63 | … | … | 1(c) | 28 | … | … | … | … | 0.05(c) | … | … | … | … | 0.1(c) | 1(c) | … | … | .35(c) |
| Hastelloy B-2(b) | 5 | … | bal. | … | … | 1(c) | 28 | … | … | … | … | 0.02(c) | … | … | … | … | … | … | … | … | … |
| Hastelloy C-276(b) | 5 | … | 59 | … | … | 15.5 | 16 | 3.7 | … | … | … | 0.02(c) | … | … | … | … | … | … | … | … | … |
| Hastelloy C-4(b) | 19.5 | 2(c) | bal. | … | 0.7(c) | 16 | 16 | … | 2(Nb+Ta) | … | … | .015(c) | … | … | … | … | 0.08(c) | 1(c) | … | 2 | … |
| Hastelloy G(b) | 19.5 | 2.5(c) | bal. | … | … | 22 | 6.5 | 1(c) | 0.3(Nb+Ta) | … | … | 0.05(c) | … | … | … | … | 1(c) | 1.5 | … | 1.9 | … |
| Hastelloy G-3(b) | 5(c) | 5(c) | bal. | 0.5 (Al+Ti)(c) | … | 22 | 7 | 1.5(c) | … | … | … | 0.015(c) | … | … | … | … | 0.4 | 0.8 | … | … | … |
| Hastelloy N(b) | 5.0(c) | … | 72 | … | 0.5(c) | 7 | 16 | … | … | … | … | 0.06 | … | … | … | … | … | … | … | … | … |
| Hastelloy S(b) | 1 | … | 67 | 0.2 | … | 15.5 | 16 | … | … | … | … | 0.02(c) | … | … | … | .02 | … | … | … | … | … |
| Hastelloy W(b) | 5.5 | 2.5(c) | 61 | … | … | 5 | 25 | … | … | … | … | 0.12(c) | … | … | … | … | … | … | … | … | … |
| Hastelloy X(b) | 15.8 | 1.5(c) | 49 | 2 | … | 22 | 9 | 0.6 | … | … | … | 0.15 | … | … | … | … | … | … | … | … | 0.6 |
| Haynes 214(b) | 3 | … | bal. | 4.5 | … | 16 | … | … | … | … | 0.01 | 0.05 | 0.1 | … | 0.01 | … | 0.2 | 0.5 | … | … | … |
| Haynes 230(b) | 3.0(c) | 5.0(c) | 55 | 0.35 | … | 22 | 2 | 14 | … | … | 0.015(c) | 0.1 | … | … | … | 0.02 | 0.4 | 0.5 | … | … | … |
| Haynes 242(a) | 2.0(c) | 2.5(c) | 63 | 0.5(c) | … | 8 | 25 | … | … | … | 0.006(c) | 0.10(c) | … | … | … | … | … | … | … | … | … |
| Haynes 263(a) | 0.7 | … | 52 | 0.6 | 2.4 | 20 | 6 | … | … | … | … | 0.06 | … | … | … | … | 0.4 | 0.6 | … | 0.2 | … |
| Haynes HR-120(b) | 33 | 3 | 37 | 0.1 | … | 25 | 2.5 | 2.5 | 0.7 | … | 0.004 | 0.05 | … | … | … | … | 0.6 | 0.7 | … | … | … |
| Haynes HR-160(b) | 2 | 29 | 37 | … | … | 28 | … | … | … | … | … | 0.05 | … | … | … | … | 2.75 | 0.5 | … | … | … |
| Haynes R-41(a) | 5 | 11 | 52 | 1.5 | 3.1 | 19 | 10 | … | … | … | 0.006 | 0.09 | … | … | … | … | 0.5 | 0.1 | … | … | … |
| Inconel 100(a) | 0.6(c) | 15 | 60 | 5.5 | 4.7 | 10 | 3 | … | … | … | 0.015 | 0.15 | 0.06 | … | … | … | … | … | … | … | 1 |
| Inconel 102(a) | 7 | … | bal. | 0.4 | 0.6 | 15 | 3 | 3 | 3 | … | 0.005 | 0.06 | 0.03 | … | … | … | … | … | 0.02 | … | … |
| Inconel 102(a) | 7 | … | 67 | 0.5 | 0.5 | 15 | 2.9 | 3 | 2.9 | … | 0.005 | 0.06 | 0.03 | … | … | … | … | … | 0.02 | … | … |
| Inconel 120(a) | … | 14 | bal. | 0.25 | 2.5 | 21 | 4 | … | 2 | … | 0.005 | 0.04 | … | … | … | … | … | … | … | … | … |
| Inconel 600(b) | 8 | … | 76 | … | … | 15.5 | … | … | … | … | … | 0.08 | … | … | … | … | 0.05 | … | … | 0.25 | … |
| Inconel 601(b) | 14.1 | … | 61 | 1.35 | … | 23 | … | … | … | … | … | 0.05 | … | … | … | … | … | … | … | 0.5 | … |
| Inconel 617(b) | … | 12.5 | 55 | 1 | … | 22 | 9 | … | … | … | … | 0.07 | … | … | … | … | … | … | … | … | … |
| Inconel 625(b) | 2.5 | … | 61 | 0.2 | 0.2 | 21.5 | 9 | … | 3.6 | … | … | 0.05 | … | … | … | … | 0.2 | 0.2 | … | 2 | … |
| Inconel 690(b) | 9 | … | 61 | … | … | 29 | … | … | … | … | … | 0.02 | … | … | … | … | … | … | … | … | … |
| Inconel 702(a) | 1 | 14 | 80 | 3.2 | 0.6 | 15.5 | … | … | … | … | … | 0.05 | … | … | … | … | 0.4 | 0.5 | … | 0.2 | … |
| Inconel 706(a) | 37.5 | … | 42 | 0.2 | 1.75 | 16 | … | 2 (Nb+Ta) | … | … | … | 0.03 | … | … | … | … | … | … | … | 0.15(c) | … |
| Inconel 718(a) | 18.5 | … | 53 | 0.5 | 0.9 | 19 | 3 | … | 5.1 | … | … | 0.08(c) | … | … | … | … | … | … | … | 0.15(c) | … |

(continued)

Strengthening mechanism (a) precipitation hardened (PH), (b) solid-solution hardened (SSH). (c) Maximum element concentration. (d) Presence of the element in unreported concentration, usually due to proprietary issues. Source: Ref 1–16

**Table A.5A** (continued)

| Alloy | | | | | | | | | | Composition, wt% | | | | | | | | | | | |
|---|---|---|---|---|---|---|---|---|---|---|---|---|---|---|---|---|---|---|---|---|---|
| | Fe | Co | Ni | Al | Ti | Cr | Mo | W | Nb | Ta | B | C | Zr | Hf | Y | La | Si | Mn | Mg | Cu | V |
| Inconel 721(a) | 6.5 | ... | 71 | ... | 3 | 16 | ... | ... | ... | ... | ... | 0.4 | ... | ... | ... | ... | ... | 2.2 | ... | 0.1 | ... |
| Inconel 722(a) | 7 | ... | 75 | 0.7 | 2.4 | 15.5 | ... | ... | ... | ... | ... | 0.04 | ... | ... | ... | ... | 0.4 | 0.5 | ... | 0.2 | ... |
| Inconel 725(a) | 9 | ... | 57 | .35(c) | 1.5 | 21 | 8 | ... | 3.5 | ... | ... | 0.03(c) | ... | ... | ... | ... | ... | ... | ... | ... | ... |
| Inconel 751(a) | 7 | ... | 73 | 1.2 | 2.3 | 15.5 | ... | ... | 1 | ... | ... | 0.05 | ... | ... | ... | ... | ... | ... | ... | 0.25(c) | ... |
| Inconel X750(a) | 7 | ... | 73 | 0.7 | 2.5 | 15.5 | ... | ... | 1 | ... | ... | 0.04 | ... | ... | ... | ... | ... | ... | ... | 0.25(c) | ... |
| M-252(a) | 0.75(c) | 10 | 57 | 1 | 2.6 | 19 | 10 | ... | ... | ... | 0.005 | 0.15 | ... | ... | ... | ... | ... | ... | ... | ... | ... |
| MERL-76(a) | ... | 18.6 | 54 | 5.1 | 4.3 | 12.4 | 3.3 | ... | 1.4 | ... | ... | 0.02 | 0.06 | 0.35 | ... | ... | ... | ... | ... | ... | ... |
| Nimonic 100(a) | 2.0(c) | 20 | 56 | 5 | 1.5 | 11 | 5 | ... | ... | ... | (d) | 0.3(c) | (d) | ... | ... | ... | ... | ... | ... | ... | ... |
| Nimonic 105(b) | ... | 20 | 54 | 4.7 | 1.2 | 15 | 5 | ... | ... | ... | 0.005 | 0.08 | ... | ... | ... | ... | ... | ... | ... | ... | ... |
| Nimonic 115(a) | 1 | 15 | 55 | 5 | 4 | 15 | 4 | ... | ... | ... | ... | 0.2 | 0.04 | ... | ... | ... | ... | ... | ... | ... | ... |
| Nimonic 75(b) | 2.5 | ... | 75 | 0.15 | 0.4 | 19.5 | ... | ... | ... | ... | ... | 0.12 | ... | ... | ... | ... | ... | ... | ... | 0.25(c) | ... |
| Nimonic 80A(a) | 1.5 | 1 | 73 | 1.4 | 2.25 | 19.5 | ... | ... | ... | ... | ... | 0.05 | ... | ... | ... | ... | ... | ... | ... | 0.10(c) | ... |
| Nimonic 86(b) | ... | ... | 65 | ... | ... | 25 | 10 | ... | ... | ... | ... | 0.05 | ... | ... | ... | ... | ... | ... | 0.015 | ... | ... |
| Nimonic 90(a) | 1.5 | 18 | 56 | 1.4 | 2.4 | 19.5 | ... | ... | ... | ... | ... | 0.06 | ... | ... | ... | ... | ... | ... | ... | ... | ... |
| Nimonic 95(a) | 5.0(c) | 18 | 54 | 2 | 2.9 | 19.5 | ... | ... | ... | ... | (d) | 0.15(c) | (d) | ... | ... | ... | ... | ... | ... | ... | ... |
| Pyromet 31(a) | 14.5 | ... | 56 | 1.5 | 2.5 | 22.7 | 2 | ... | 1.1 | ... | 0.005 | 0.04 | ... | ... | ... | ... | ... | ... | ... | ... | ... |
| Pyromet 860(a) | 28.9 | 4 | 44 | 1 | 3 | 13 | 6 | ... | ... | ... | 0.01 | 0.05 | ... | ... | ... | ... | ... | ... | ... | ... | ... |
| RA333(b) | 18 | 3 | 45 | ... | ... | 25 | 3 | 3 | ... | ... | ... | 0.05 | ... | ... | ... | ... | ... | ... | ... | ... | ... |
| Refractaloy 26(a) | 16 | 20 | 38 | 0.2 | 2.6 | 18 | 3.2 | ... | ... | ... | 0.015 | 0.03 | ... | ... | ... | ... | ... | ... | ... | ... | ... |
| René 100(a) | 1.0(c) | 15 | 61 | 5.5 | 4.2 | 9.5 | 3 | ... | ... | ... | 0.015 | 0.16 | 0.06 | ... | ... | ... | ... | ... | ... | ... | 1 |
| René 41(a) | 0.3(c) | 11 | 55 | 1.5 | 3.1 | 19 | 10 | ... | ... | ... | 0.01 | 0.09 | ... | ... | ... | ... | ... | ... | ... | ... | ... |
| René 88(a) | ... | 13 | 56 | 2.1 | 3.7 | 16 | 4 | 4 | 0.7 | ... | ... | 0.03 | 0.03 | ... | ... | ... | ... | ... | ... | ... | ... |
| René 95(a) | 0.3(c) | 8 | 61 | 3.5 | 2.5 | 14 | 3.5 | 3.5 | 3.5 | ... | 0.01 | 0.16 | 0.05 | ... | ... | ... | ... | ... | ... | ... | ... |
| Udimet 500(a) | 4.0(c) | 19 | 48 | 3 | 3 | 19 | 4 | ... | ... | ... | 0.005 | 0.08 | ... | ... | ... | ... | ... | ... | ... | ... | ... |
| Udimet 520(a) | ... | 12 | 57 | 2 | 3 | 19 | 6 | 1 | ... | ... | 0.005 | 0.08 | ... | ... | ... | ... | ... | ... | ... | ... | ... |
| Udimet 630(a) | 18 | ... | 50 | 0.7 | 1 | 17 | 3 | 3 | 6.5 | ... | 0.004 | 0.04 | ... | ... | ... | ... | ... | ... | ... | ... | ... |
| Udimet 700(a) | 1.0(c) | 18.5 | 53 | 4.3 | 3.4 | 15 | 5 | ... | ... | ... | 0.03 | 0.07 | ... | ... | ... | ... | ... | ... | ... | ... | ... |
| Udimet 710(a) | ... | 14.8 | 55 | 2.5 | 5 | 18 | 3 | 1.5 | ... | ... | 0.01 | 0.07 | ... | ... | ... | ... | ... | ... | ... | ... | ... |
| Udimet 720(a) | ... | 14.8 | 55 | 2.5 | 5 | 18 | 3 | 1.3 | ... | ... | ... | 0.035 | 0.03 | ... | ... | ... | ... | ... | ... | ... | ... |
| Udimet 720LI(a) | ... | 15 | 57 | 2.5 | 5 | 16 | 3 | 1.3 | ... | ... | ... | 0.025 | 0.03 | ... | ... | ... | ... | ... | ... | ... | ... |
| Unitemp AF2-1DA(a) | 0.5(c) | 10 | 59 | 4.6 | 3 | 12 | 3 | 6 | ... | 1.5 | 0.015 | 0.35 | 0.1 | ... | ... | ... | ... | ... | ... | ... | ... |
| Waspaloy(a) | 2.0(c) | 13.5 | 57 | 1.4 | 3 | 19.5 | 4.3 | ... | ... | ... | 0.06 | 0.07 | 0.09 | ... | ... | ... | ... | ... | ... | ... | ... |
| Waspaloy A(a) | 2(c) | 13.5 | bal. | 1.4 | 3 | 19.5 | 4.3 | ... | ... | ... | 0.09 | 0.07 | ... | ... | ... | ... | ... | 0.5(c) | ... | ... | ... |
| Waspaloy B(a) | ... | 13.5 | bal. | 1.4 | 3 | 19.5 | 4.3 | ... | ... | ... | 0.07 | 0.07 | ... | ... | ... | ... | ... | 0.5(c) | ... | ... | ... |

Strengthening mechanism (a) precipitation hardened (PH), (b) solid-solution hardened (SSH). (c) Maximum element concentration. (d) Presence of the element in unreported concentration, usually due to proprietary issues.
Source: Ref 1–16

**Table A.5B  Applications and comments to selected superalloys in Table A.5A**

| Alloy | Application | Comments |
|---|---|---|
| Astroloy | Forgings for high temperatures | … |
| Hastelloy B | Older GTEs and rocket engines | Good strength up to 1095 °C (2005 °F) but limited by relative oxidation resistance to 650 °C (1200 °F). Replaced by Haynes 242, Hastelloy B-2, and Hastelloy B-3 |
| Hastelloy B-2 | … | Resists hot hydrochloric acid and hydrogen chloride gas in as-welded condition |
| Hastelloy C-276 | … | For very corrosive conditions. Resistant to oxidizing and mildly oxidizing corrosives. Excellent stress-corrosion cracking resistance and resistance to localized attack |
| Hastelloy C-4 | … | High stability in 650–1040 °C (1200–1905 °F) range evidenced by good ductility and corrosion resistance. Equivalent environmental resistance to C-276 |
| Hastelloy G | SO₂ and SO₃ scrubbers, phosphoric acid service | Resists pitting and stress-corrosion cracking in both acid and alkaline environments |
| Hastelloy G-3 | … | Resistant to hot molten fluoride salts |
| Hastelloy N | Gas turbine parts, welding wire for high-temperature components, container for molten fluoride salts | Good resistance to aging and embrittlement and good fabricability. Excellent resistance to hot fluoride salts in 705–870 °C (1300–1600 °F) temperature range |
| Hastelloy S | Low-stress GTE components, welding wire for high-temperature components | High thermal stability and good thermal fatigue resistance. Good oxidation resistance and relatively low CTE |
| Hastelloy W | GTE combustors and fabricated parts | Balance of strength, oxidation resistance, and fabricability |
| Hastelloy X | GTE transition ducts, combustors, spray bars, flame holders, afterburners, tailpipes, and cabin heaters; industrial furnaces; catalyst support grids; furnace baffles; tubing for pyrolysis operations; and flash drier components | Good oxidation resistance, fabricability, and strength |
| Haynes 230 | Combustion environments, nitric acid catalyst grids, high-temperature bellows, industrial furnace fixtures and hardware, strand annealing tubes, thermocouple protection tubes | Strength, stability, and oxidation resistance up to 1150 °C (2100 °F) |
| Haynes 242 | Seal rings, duct segments, casings, fasteners, rocket nozzles, and pumps | High strength, fatigue resistance, and oxidation resistance up to 760 °C (1400 °F), relatively low CTE |
| Haynes HR-120 | Heat treating fixtures and industrial heating applications as an alternative to IN-800H | Economical high-strength alloy with good resistance to industrial environments. Excellent carburization and sulfidation resistance |
| Haynes HR-160 | Waste incineration, boiler, high-temperature reaction vessel, and rotary calciner applications | Outstanding resistance to sulfidation and other high-temperature aggressive environments |
| Inconel R-41 | GTE critical components | Excellent strength in 540–980 °C (1005–1795 °F) temperature range |
| Inconel 102 | Superheater and GTE parts | Composition weight 67% Ni |
| Inconel 600 | Furnace components, in chemical and food processing, in nuclear engineering, and for sparking electrodes | Ni-Cr alloy with good oxidation resistance at high temperatures and resistance to chloride-ion stress-corrosion cracking, corrosion by high-purity water, and caustic corrosion |
| Inconel 601 | Industrial furnaces; heat treating equipment such as baskets, muffles, and retorts; petrochemical and other process equipment; and gas turbine components | Ni-Cr alloy with an addition of Al for outstanding resistance to oxidation and other forms of high-temperature corrosion. Also has high mechanical Properties at elevated temperatures |
| Inconel 617 | Gas turbines for combustion cans, ducting, and transition liners; for petrochemical processing, heat treating equipment, and in nitric acid production | Ni-Cr-Co-Mo alloy with an exceptional combination of metallurgical stability, strength, and oxidation resistance. Resistance to oxidation is enhanced by an Al addition. |
| Inconel 625 | Chemical processing, aerospace and marine engineering, pollution-control equipment, and nuclear reactors | Ni-Cr-Mo alloy with an addition of Nb that acts with the Mo to stiffen the alloy matrix and thereby provide high strength without a strengthening heat treatment. Resists a wide range of severely corrosive environments and is especially resistant to pitting and crevice corrosion |

(continued)

Source: Ref 1–16

**Table A.5B** (continued)

| Alloy | Application | Comments |
|---|---|---|
| Inconel 690 | ... | Resists nitric and hydrofluoric acids |
| Inconel 718 | GTE components, rocket motors, spacecraft, nuclear reactor pumps, and tooling | Most widely used of all wrought superalloys. Creep rupture strength up to 700 °C (1290 °F) |
| Inconel X750 | High-temperature springs and bolts. GTEs, rocket engines, nuclear reactors, pressure vessels, tooling, aircraft structures | Similar to IN-600 but precipitation hardenable. High tensile and creep-rupture properties up to 700 °C (1290 °F). High stress-relaxation resistance |
| M-252 | GTE blades, parts, sheets | ... |
| Nimonic 105 | GTE blades, discs, shafts | Relatively high Al contents enhance strength (PH) and oxidation resistance. Creep-rupture properties up to 950 °C (1740 °F) |
| Nimonic 115 | Turbine blades in aircraft GTEs | Similar to Nimonic 105, higher Al+Ti levels provide increased strengthening. High strength and creep resistance up to 1010 °C (1850 °F) |
| Nimonic 75 | GTE sheet metal fabrications, industrial furnace components, heat treating equipment and fixtures, nuclear applications | ... |
| Nimonic 80A | GTE blades, rings and discs, bolts, tube supports in nuclear steam generators, die casting inserts and cores, exhaust valves in internal combustion engines | Similar to Nimonic 75 but PH. Good corrosion and oxidation resistance and tensile and creep-rupture properties up to 815 °C (1500 °F) |
| Nimonic 86 | GTE sheet metal fabrications such as combustion chambers and afterburners, heat-treating furnaces | Good formability and weldability. Ce addition provides oxidation and scaling resistance up to 1050 °C (1920 °F) |
| Nimonic 90 | GTE blades and discs, hot working tools, springs | High stress-rupture strength and creep resistance up to 920 °C (1690 °F) combined with hot corrosion and oxidation resistance |
| René 41 | GTE parts and blades | ... |
| René 95 | Turbine or compressor disc alloy | ... |
| Udimet 500 | GTE parts, sheets, bolts | ... |
| Udimet 520 | GTE blades | Improved workability over Udimet 500. Developed for use in 760–927 °C (1400–1700 °F) temperature range; high structural stability and exceptional fabricability |
| Udimet 630 | ... | Limited to applications below 540 °C (1005 °F) |
| Udimet 710 | Disc alloy | Sulfidation resistant |
| Udimet 720 | GTE blades and discs | High strength and metallurgical stability. Impact resistant after high-temperature exposure. Good oxidation, sulfidation, and impact resistance |
| Unitemp AF2-1DA | Turbine discs | ... |
| Waspaloy | GTE compressor and rotor discs, shafts, spacers, seals, rings, casings, fasteners and other hardware, airframe assemblies, missile systems | High-temperature strength and oxidation resistance. Used in highly loaded components up to 650 °C (1200 °F) |
| Waspaloy A | Jet engine blades | Has a higher solution temperature and longer stabilization time than Waspaloy B |
| Waspaloy B | Jet engine discs | ... |

Source: Ref 1–16

# Nickel Powder Metallurgy Alloys

## Table A.6A   Selected nickel powder metallurgy superalloy compositions

| Alloy | Composition, wt% | | | | | | | | | | | | | | |
|---|---|---|---|---|---|---|---|---|---|---|---|---|---|---|---|
| | Co | Ni | Al | Ti | Cr | Mo | W | Nb | Ta | Re | B | C | Zr | Hf | Y₂O₃ |
| AF115 | 15 | 55 | 3.8 | 3.9 | 10.7 | 2.8 | 5.9 | 2.7 | ... | ... | 0.02 | 0.5 | 0.05 | 0.4 | ... |
| Alloy 92(a) | 6 | bal. | 6.5 | 1 | 8 | 1.5 | 6 | ... | 3 | 3 | 0.01 | 0.05 | 0.15 | ... | 0.9 |
| MA-6000(a) | ... | bal. | 4.5 | 2.5 | 15 | 2 | 4 | ... | 2 | ... | 0.01 | ... | 0.15 | ... | 1.1 |
| MA-754(a) | ... | bal. | 0.3 | 0.5 | 20 | ... | ... | ... | ... | ... | ... | 0.05 | ... | ... | 0.6 |
| MA-758(a) | ... | bal. | 0.3 | 0.5 | 30 | ... | ... | ... | ... | ... | ... | 0.05 | ... | ... | 0.6 |
| MA-760(a) | ... | bal. | 6 | ... | 20 | 2 | 3.5 | ... | ... | ... | 0.01 | 0.05 | 0.15 | ... | 0.95 |
| René 88DT(b) | 12.7 | 57 | 2.15 | 3.7 | 16 | 4 | 4 | 0.7 | ... | ... | 0.015 | 0.05 | 0.05 | ... | ... |

Strengthening mechanism (a) oxide dispersion strengthened (ODS), (b) precipitation hardened (PH). Source: Ref 1 –16

## Table A.6B   Applications and comments to selected superalloys in Table A.6A

| Alloy | Application | Comments |
|---|---|---|
| MA-754 | Turbine stator vanes | ... |
| MA-758 | Spinners for fiberglass manufacture (1200 °C) (2190 °F), diesel engines, furnace skid rails for steel slag and billet transfer (1260 °C) (2300 °F) | Similar to MA-754. Increased Cr content for corrosion resistance in oxidizing environments and molten glass |

Source: Ref 1 –16

APPENDIX

# Element Properties

## Table B.1 Properties of common superalloy alloying elements

| Element | Crystal structure (symbol)(a) | Lattice constant, Å | | | Melting point | | Atomic weight, g/mol | Density, g/cm³ | Minimum interatomic distance, nm | Atomic radius, nm |
|---|---|---|---|---|---|---|---|---|---|---|
| | | a | b | c | °C | °F | | | | |
| Al | fcc (A1) | 4.0491 | ... | ... | 660 | 1220 | 26.98 | 2.70 | 0.2862 | 0.143 |
| B | α rhom | 17.89 | 8.95 | 10.15 | 2030(b) | 3690(b) | 10.82 | 2.45 | ... | ... |
| | β rhom | ... | ... | ... | ... | ... | ... | ... | ... | ... |
| | γ tet | ... | ... | ... | ... | ... | ... | ... | ... | ... |
| C (graphite) | Hex (A9) | 2.4614 | ... | 6.7041 | 3727(c) | 6740(c) | 12.01 | 2.25 | 0.142 | 0.071 |
| C (diam) | fcc (A4) | ... | ... | ... | ... | ... | ... | ... | ... | ... |
| Ce | α fcc (A1) | 5.16 | ... | ... | 804 | 1479 | 140.013 | 6.77 | ... | ... |
| | β hcp | ... | ... | ... | ... | ... | ... | ... | ... | ... |
| | γ fcc (A1) | ... | ... | ... | ... | ... | ... | ... | ... | ... |
| | δ bcc (A2) | ... | ... | ... | ... | ... | ... | ... | ... | ... |
| Cr | bcc (A2) | 2.884 | ... | ... | 1875 | 3407 | 52.01 | 7.19 | 0.2498 | 0.125 |
| Co | α hcp (A3) | 2.5071 | ... | 4.0686 | 1495 ± 1 | 2723 ± 2 | 58.94 | 8.85 | 0.24967 | 0.125 |
| | β fcc (A1) | ... | ... | ... | ... | ... | ... | ... | ... | ... |
| Cu | fcc (A1) | 3.6153 | ... | ... | 1083 | 1981 | 63.54 | 8.96 | 0.2556 | 0.128 |
| Fe | α bcc (A2) | 2.8664(d) | ... | ... | 1536.5 ± 1 | 2797 ± 2 | 55.85 | 7.87 | 0.24824 | 0.124 |
| | γ fcc (A1) | ... | ... | ... | ... | ... | ... | ... | ... | ... |
| | δ bcc (A2) | ... | ... | ... | ... | ... | ... | ... | ... | ... |
| Hf | α hcp (A3) | 3.1883 | ... | 5.0422 | 2222 ± 30 | 4032 ± 55 | 178.58 | 13.1 | ... | ... |
| | β bcc (A2) | ... | ... | ... | ... | ... | ... | ... | ... | ... |
| La | α hcp | 3.77 | ... | 12.16 | 920 | 1690 | 138.92 | 6.15 | ... | ... |
| | β fcc (A1) | ... | ... | ... | ... | ... | ... | ... | ... | ... |
| | γ bcc (A2) | ... | ... | ... | ... | ... | ... | ... | ... | ... |
| Mg | hcp (A3) | 3.2088(d) | ... | 5.2095(d) | 650 ± 2 | 1200 ± 4 | 24.32 | 1.74 | 0.3196 | 0.160 |
| Mn | α comp | 8.912 | ... | ... | 1245 | 2273 | 54.94 | 7.43 | ... | 0.112 |
| | bcc (A12) | ... | ... | ... | ... | ... | ... | ... | ... | ... |
| | β comp cu (A13) | ... | ... | ... | ... | ... | ... | ... | ... | ... |
| | γ fcc (A1) | ... | ... | ... | ... | ... | ... | ... | ... | ... |
| | δ bcc (A2) | ... | ... | ... | ... | ... | ... | ... | ... | ... |
| Mo | bcc (A2) | 3.1468(d) | ... | ... | 2610 | 4730 | 95.95 | 10.2 | 0.2725 | 0.136 |
| Ni | fcc (A1) | 3.5238 | ... | ... | 1453 | 2647 | 58.71 | 8.9 | 0.2491 | 0.125 |
| Nb | bcc (A2) | 3.301 | ... | ... | 2468 ± 10 | 4474 ± 20 | 92.91 | 8.57 | 0.2859 | 0.143 |
| Re | hcp (A3) | 2.760 | ... | 4.458 | 3180 ± 20 | 5756 ± 35 | 186.22 | 21.0 | 0.274 | ... |
| Ru | hcp (A3) | 2.7041 | ... | 4.2814 | 2500 ± 100 | 4530 ± 180 | 101.07 | 12.45 | ... | ... |
| S | α comp fco | 10.50 | 12.95 | 24.60 | 119 | 245 | 32.07 | 2.07 | 0.212 | 0.106 |
| | β comp mono | ... | ... | ... | ... | ... | ... | ... | ... | ... |
| | γ rhom | ... | ... | ... | ... | ... | ... | ... | ... | ... |

(continued)

(a) fcc, face-centered cubic; hcp, hexagonally close-packed; bcc, body-centered cubic; fco, face-centered orthorhombic; rhom, rhombohedral; tet, tetragonal; hex, hexagonal; comp, complex; cu, cubic; mono, monoclinic. (b) Approximate. (c) Sublimes. (d) At 25 °C. (e) Distilled metal. Source: Ref 1

**Table B.1 (continued)**

| Element | Crystal structure (symbol)(a) | Lattice constant, Å | | | Melting point | | Atomic weight, g/mol | Density, g/cm³ | Minimum interatomic distance, nm | Atomic radius, nm |
|---|---|---|---|---|---|---|---|---|---|---|
| | | a | b | c | °C | °F | | | | |
| Si | fcc (A4) | 5.428 | ... | ... | 1410 | 2570 | 28.09 | 2.33 | 0.2351 | 0.144 |
| Ta | bcc (A2) | 3.303 | ... | ... | 2996 ± 50 | 5425 ± 90 | 180.95 | 16.6 | 0.2859 | ... |
| Ti | α hcp (A3) | 2.95030 | ... | 4.68312 | 1668 ± 10 | 3034 ± 20 | 47.90 | 4.51 | ... | 0.145 |
| | β bcc (A2) | ... | ... | ... | ... | ... | ... | ... | ... | ... |
| W | bcc (A2) | 3.158 | ... | ... | 3410 | 6170 | 183.86 | 19.3 | 0.2734 | 0.137 |
| V | bcc (A2) | 3.039 | ... | ... | 1900 ± 25 | 3450 ± 45 | 50.95 | 6.11 | 0.2632 | ... |
| Y | α hcp (A3) | 3.65 | ... | 5.73 | 1509(e) | 2750(e) | 88.92 | 4.47 | ... | ... |
| | β bcc (A2) | ... | ... | ... | ... | ... | ... | ... | ... | ... |
| Zr | α hcp (A3) | 3.2312(d) | ... | 5.1477(d) | 1852 | 3366 | 91.22 | 6.49 | 0.317 | 0.159 |
| | β bcc (A2) | ... | ... | ... | ... | ... | ... | ... | ... | ... |

(a) fcc, face-centered cubic; hcp, hexagonally close-packed; bcc, body-centered cubic; fco, face-centered orthorhombic; rhom, rhombohedral; tet, tetragonal; hex, hexagonal; comp, complex; cu, cubic; mono, monoclinic. (b) Approximate. (c) Sublimes. (d) At 25 °C. (e) Distilled metal. Source: Ref 1

# REFERENCE

1. H.S. Ko, K.W. Paik, L.J. Park, Y.G. Kim, and J.H. Tundermann, Influence of Rhenium on the Microstructures and Mechanical Properties of a Mechanically Alloyed Oxide Dispersion-Strengthened Nickel-Base Superalloy, *J. Mater. Sci.*, Vol 33, 1998, p 3361–3370

APPENDIX  C

# Selected Superalloy Properties

All tables and the figure were reproduced from Ref 1.

## Table C.1 Mechanical properties of selected wrought superalloys

| | | Ultimate tensile strength at: | | | | | | Yield strength at 0.2% offset at: | | | | | | Tensile elongation, % at: | | |
| | | 21 °C (70 °F) | | 540 °C (1000 °F) | | 760 °C (1400 °F) | | 21 °C (70 °F) | | 540 °C (1000 °F) | | 760 °C (1400 °F) | | 21 °C | 540 °C | 760 °C |
| Alloy | Form | MPa | ksi | MPa | ksi | MPa | ksi | MPa | ksi | MPa | ksi | MPa | ksi | (70 °F) | (1000 °F) | (1400 °F) |
|---|---|---|---|---|---|---|---|---|---|---|---|---|---|---|---|---|
| **Nickel-base** | | | | | | | | | | | | | | | | |
| Astroloy | Bar | 1415 | 205 | 1240 | 180 | 1160 | 168 | 1050 | 152 | 965 | 140 | 910 | 132 | 16 | 16 | 21 |
| Cabot 214 | ... | 915 | 133 | 715 | 104 | 560 | 84 | 650 | 81 | 510 | 74 | 495 | 72 | 38 | 19 | 9 |
| D-979 | Bar | 1410 | 204 | 1295 | 188 | 720 | 104 | 1005 | 146 | 925 | 134 | 655 | 95 | 15 | 15 | 17 |
| Hastelloy C-22 | Sheet | 800 | 116 | 625 | 91 | 525 | 76 | 405 | 59 | 275 | 40 | 240 | 35 | 57 | 61 | 63 |
| Hastelloy G-30 | Sheet | 690 | 100 | 490 | 71 | ... | ... | 315 | 46 | 170 | 25 | ... | ... | 64 | 75 | ... |
| Hastelloy S | Bar | 845 | 130 | 775 | 112 | 575 | 84 | 455 | 65 | 340 | 49 | 310 | 45 | 49 | 50 | 70 |
| Hastelloy X | Sheet | 785 | 114 | 650 | 94 | 435 | 63 | 360 | 52 | 290 | 42 | 260 | 38 | 43 | 45 | 37 |
| Haynes 230 | (a) | 870 | 126 | 720 | 105 | 575 | 84 | 390 | 57 | 275 | 40 | 285 | 41 | 48 | 56 | 46 |
| Inconel 587 | Bar | 1180 | 171 | 1035 | 150 | 830 | 120 | 705 | 102 | 620 | 90 | 605 | 88 | 28 | 22 | 20 |
| Inconel 597 | Bar | 1220 | 177 | 1140 | 165 | 930 | 135 | 760 | 110 | 720 | 104 | 665 | 96 | 15 | 15 | 16 |
| Inconel 600 | Bar | 660 | 96 | 560 | 81 | 260 | 38 | 285 | 41 | 220 | 32 | 180 | 26 | 45 | 41 | 70 |
| Inconel 601 | Sheet | 740 | 107 | 725 | 105 | 290 | 42 | 455 | 66 | 350 | 51 | 220 | 32 | 40 | 34 | 78 |
| Inconel 617 | Bar | 740 | 107 | 580 | 84 | 440 | 64 | 295 | 43 | 200 | 29 | 180 | 26 | 70 | 68 | 84 |
| Inconel 617 | Sheet | 770 | 112 | 590 | 86 | 470 | 68 | 345 | 50 | 230 | 33 | 230 | 33 | 55 | 62 | 59 |
| Inconel 625 | Bar | 965 | 140 | 910 | 132 | 550 | 80 | 490 | 71 | 415 | 60 | 415 | 60 | 50 | 50 | 45 |
| Inconel 706 | Bar | 1310 | 190 | 1145 | 166 | 725 | 105 | 1005 | 146 | 910 | 132 | 660 | 96 | 20 | 19 | 32 |
| Inconel 718 | Bar | 1435 | 208 | 1275 | 185 | 950 | 138 | 1185 | 172 | 1065 | 154 | 740 | 107 | 21 | 18 | 25 |
| Inconel 718 Direct Age | Bar | 1530 | 222 | 1350 | 196 | ... | ... | 1365 | 198 | 1180 | 171 | ... | ... | 16 | 15 | ... |
| Inconel 718 Super | Bar | 1350 | 196 | 1200 | 174 | ... | ... | 1105 | 160 | 1020 | 148 | ... | ... | 16 | 18 | ... |
| Inconel X750 | Bar | 1200 | 174 | 1050 | 152 | ... | ... | 815 | 118 | 725 | 105 | ... | ... | 27 | 26 | ... |
| M-252 | Bar | 1240 | 180 | 1230 | 178 | 945 | 137 | 840 | 122 | 765 | 111 | 720 | 104 | 16 | 15 | 10 |
| Nimonic 75 | Bar | 745 | 108 | 675 | 98 | 310 | 45 | 285 | 41 | 200 | 29 | 160 | 23 | 40 | 40 | 67 |
| Nimonic 80A | Bar | 1000 | 145 | 875 | 127 | 600 | 87 | 620 | 90 | 530 | 77 | 505 | 73 | 39 | 37 | 17 |
| Nimonic 90 | Bar | 1235 | 179 | 1075 | 156 | 655 | 95 | 810 | 117 | 725 | 105 | 540 | 78 | 33 | 28 | 12 |
| Nimonic 105 | Bar | 1180 | 171 | 1130 | 164 | 930 | 135 | 830 | 120 | 775 | 112 | 740 | 107 | 16 | 22 | 25 |

(continued)

(a) Cold-rolled and solution-annealed sheet, 1.2 to 1.6 mm (0.048 to 0.063 in.) thick. (b) Annealed. (c) Precipitation hardened. (d) Work strengthened and aged

## Table C.1 (continued)

| Alloy | Form | Ultimate tensile strength at: 21 °C (70 °F) MPa | ksi | 540 °C (1000 °F) MPa | ksi | 760 °C (1400 °F) MPa | ksi | Yield strength at 0.2% offset at: 21 °C (70 °F) MPa | ksi | 540 °C (1000 °F) MPa | ksi | 760 °C (1400 °F) MPa | ksi | Tensile elongation, % at: 21 °C (70 °F) | 540 °C (1000 °F) | 760 °C (1400 °F) |
|---|---|---|---|---|---|---|---|---|---|---|---|---|---|---|---|---|
| **Nickel-base (continued)** | | | | | | | | | | | | | | | | |
| Nimonic 115 | Bar | 1240 | 180 | 1090 | 158 | 1085 | 157 | 865 | 125 | 795 | 115 | 800 | 116 | 27 | 18 | 24 |
| Nimonic 263 | Sheet | 970 | 141 | 800 | 116 | 650 | 94 | 580 | 84 | 485 | 70 | 460 | 67 | 39 | 42 | 21 |
| Nimonic 942 | Bar | 1405 | 204 | 1300 | 189 | 900 | 131 | 1060 | 154 | 970 | 141 | 860 | 125 | 37 | 26 | 42 |
| Nimonic PE 11 | Bar | 1080 | 157 | 1000 | 145 | 760 | 110 | 720 | 105 | 690 | 100 | 560 | 81 | 30 | 30 | 18 |
| Nimonic PE 16 | Bar | 885 | 128 | 740 | 107 | 510 | 74 | 530 | 77 | 485 | 70 | 370 | 54 | 37 | 26 | 42 |
| Nimonic PK 33 | Sheet | 1180 | 171 | 1000 | 145 | 885 | 128 | 780 | 113 | 725 | 105 | 670 | 97 | 30 | 30 | 18 |
| Pyromet 860 | Bar | 1295 | 188 | 1255 | 182 | 910 | 132 | 835 | 121 | 840 | 122 | 835 | 121 | 22 | 15 | 18 |
| Rene 41 | Bar | 1420 | 206 | 1400 | 203 | 1105 | 160 | 1060 | 154 | 1020 | 147 | 940 | 136 | 14 | 14 | 11 |
| Rene 95 | Bar | 1620 | 235 | 1550 | 224 | 1170 | 170 | 1310 | 190 | 1255 | 182 | 1100 | 160 | 15 | 12 | 15 |
| Udimet 400 | Bar | 1310 | 190 | 1185 | 172 | ... | ... | 930 | 135 | 830 | 120 | ... | ... | 30 | 26 | ... |
| Udimet 500 | Bar | 1310 | 190 | 1240 | 180 | 1040 | 151 | 840 | 122 | 795 | 115 | 730 | 106 | 32 | 28 | 39 |
| Udimet 520 | Bar | 1310 | 190 | 1240 | 180 | 725 | 105 | 860 | 125 | 825 | 130 | 725 | 105 | 21 | 20 | 15 |
| Udimet 630 | Bar | 1520 | 220 | 1380 | 200 | 965 | 140 | 1310 | 190 | 1170 | 170 | 860 | 125 | 15 | 15 | 5 |
| Udimet 700 | Bar | 1410 | 204 | 1275 | 185 | 1035 | 150 | 965 | 140 | 895 | 130 | 825 | 120 | 17 | 16 | 20 |
| Udimet 710 | Bar | 1185 | 172 | 1150 | 167 | 1020 | 148 | 910 | 132 | 850 | 123 | 815 | 118 | 7 | 10 | 25 |
| Udimet 720 | Bar | 1570 | 228 | ... | ... | 1455 | 211 | 1195 | 173 | ... | ... | 1050 | 152 | 13 | ... | 9 |
| Unitemp AF2-1DA6 | Bar | 1560 | 226 | 1480 | 215 | 1290 | 187 | 1015 | 147 | 1040 | 151 | 995 | 144 | 20 | 19 | 16 |
| Waspaloy | Bar | 1275 | 185 | 1170 | 170 | 650 | 94 | 795 | 115 | 725 | 105 | 675 | 98 | 25 | 23 | 28 |
| **Iron-base** | | | | | | | | | | | | | | | | |
| A-286 | Bar | 1005 | 146 | 905 | 131 | 440 | 64 | 725 | 105 | 605 | 88 | 430 | 62 | 25 | 19 | 19 |
| Alloy 901 | Bar | 1205 | 175 | 1030 | 149 | 725 | 105 | 895 | 130 | 780 | 113 | 635 | 92 | 14 | 14 | 19 |
| Discaloy | Bar | 1000 | 145 | 865 | 125 | 485 | 70 | 730 | 106 | 650 | 94 | 430 | 62 | 19 | 16 | ... |
| Haynes 556 | Sheet | 815 | 118 | 645 | 93 | 470 | 69 | 410 | 60 | 240 | 35 | 220 | 32 | 48 | 54 | 49 |
| Incoloy 800 | Bar | 595 | 86 | 510 | 74 | 235 | 34 | 250 | 36 | 180 | 26 | 150 | 22 | 44 | 38 | 83 |
| Incoloy 801 | Bar | 785 | 114 | 660 | 96 | 325 | 47 | 385 | 56 | 310 | 45 | 290 | 42 | 30 | 28 | 55 |
| Incoloy 802 | Bar | 690 | 100 | 600 | 87 | 400 | 58 | 290 | 42 | 195 | 28 | 200 | 29 | 44 | 39 | 15 |
| Incoloy 807 | Bar | 655 | 95 | 470 | 68 | 350 | 51 | 380 | 55 | 255 | 37 | 225 | 32.5 | 48 | 40 | 34 |
| Incoloy 825(b) | ... | 690 | 100 | ~590 | ~86 | ~275 | ~40 | 310 | 45 | ~234 | ~34 | 180 | ~26 | 45 | ~44 | ~86 |
| Incoloy 903 | Bar | 1310 | 190 | ... | ... | ... | ... | 1105 | 160 | ... | ... | ... | ... | 14 | ... | ... |
| Incoloy 907(c) | ... | ~1365 | ~198 | ~1205 | ~175 | ~655 | ~95 | 1110 | 161 | ~960 | ~139 | ~565 | ~82 | ~12 | ~11 | ~20 |
| Incoloy 909 | Bar | 1310 | 190 | 1160 | 168 | 615 | 89 | 1020 | 148 | 945 | 137 | 540 | 78 | 16 | 14 | 34 |
| N-155 | Bar | 815 | 118 | 650 | 94 | 428 | 62 | 400 | 58 | 340 | 49 | 250 | 36 | 40 | 33 | 32 |
| V-57 | Bar | 1170 | 170 | 1000 | 145 | 620 | 90 | 830 | 120 | 760 | 110 | 485 | 70 | 26 | 19 | 34 |
| 19-9 DL | ... | 815 | 118 | 615 | 89 | ... | ... | 570 | 83 | 395 | 57 | ... | ... | 43 | 30 | ... |
| 16-25-6 | ... | 980 | 142 | ... | ... | 415 | 60 | 770 | 112 | ... | ... | 345 | 50 | 23 | ... | 11 |
| **Cobalt-base** | | | | | | | | | | | | | | | | |
| AirResist 213 | ... | 1120 | 162 | ... | ... | 485 | 70 | 625 | 91 | ... | ... | 385 | 56 | 14 | ... | 47 |
| Elgiloy | ... | 690(e)–2480(d) | 100(e)–360(d) | ... | ... | ... | ... | 480(e)–2000(d) | 70–290 | ... | ... | ... | ... | 34 | ... | ... |
| Haynes 188 | Sheet | 960 | 139 | 740 | 107 | 635 | 92 | 485 | 70 | 305 | 44 | 290 | 42 | 56 | 70 | 43 |
| L-605 | Sheet | 1005 | 146 | 800 | 116 | 455 | 66 | 460 | 67 | 250 | 36 | 260 | 38 | 64 | 59 | 12 |
| MAR-M918 | Sheet | 895 | 130 | ... | ... | ... | ... | 895 | 130 | ... | ... | ... | ... | 48 | ... | ... |
| MP35N | Bar | 2025 | 294 | ... | ... | ... | ... | 1620 | 235 | ... | ... | ... | ... | 10 | ... | ... |
| MP159 | Bar | 1895 | 275 | 1565 | 227 | ... | ... | 1825 | 265 | 1495 | 217 | ... | ... | 8 | 8 | ... |
| Stellite 6B | Sheet | 1010 | 146 | ... | ... | ... | ... | 635 | 92 | ... | ... | ... | ... | 11 | ... | ... |
| Haynes 150 | ... | 925 | 134 | ... | ... | ... | ... | 317 | 46 | ... | ... | ... | ... | 8 | ... | ... |

(a) Cold-rolled and solution-annealed sheet, 1.2 to 1.6 mm (0.048 to 0.063 in.) thick. (b) Annealed. (c) Precipitation hardened. (d) Work strengthened and aged

## Table C.2 Mechanical properties of selected cast superalloys

| Alloy | Ultimate tensile strength at: | | | | | | 0.2% yield strength at: | | | | | | Tensile elongation, % at: | | |
|---|---|---|---|---|---|---|---|---|---|---|---|---|---|---|---|
| | 21 °C (70 °F) | | 538 °C (1000 °F) | | 1093 °C (2000 °F) | | 21 °C (70 °F) | | 538 °C (1000 °F) | | 1093 °C (2000 °F) | | 21 °C | 538 °C | 1093 °C |
| | MPa | ksi | MPa | ksi | MPa | ksi | MPa | ksi | MPa | ksi | MPa | ksi | (70 °F) | (1000 °F) | (2000 °F) |
| **Nickel-base** | | | | | | | | | | | | | | | |
| IN-713 C | 850 | 123 | 860 | 125 | ... | ... | 740 | 107 | 705 | 102 | ... | ... | 8 | 10 | ... |
| IN-713 LC | 895 | 130 | 895 | 130 | ... | ... | 750 | 109 | 760 | 110 | ... | ... | 15 | 11 | ... |
| B-1900 | 970 | 141 | 1005 | 146 | 270 | 38 | 825 | 120 | 870 | 126 | 195 | 28 | 8 | 7 | 11 |
| IN-625 | 710 | 103 | 510 | 74 | ... | ... | 350 | 51 | 235 | 34 | ... | ... | 48 | 50 | ... |
| IN-718 | 1090 | 158 | ... | ... | ... | ... | 915 | 133 | ... | ... | ... | ... | 11 | ... | ... |
| IN-100 | 1018 | 147 | 1090 | 150 | (380) | (55) | 850 | 123 | 885 | 128 | (240) | (35) | 9 | 9 | ... |
| IN-162 | 1005 | 146 | 1020 | 148 | ... | ... | 815 | 118 | 795 | 115 | ... | ... | 7 | 6.5 | ... |
| IN-731 | 835 | 121 | ... | ... | 275 | 40 | 725 | 105 | ... | ... | 170 | 25 | 6.5 | ... | ... |
| IN-738 | 1095 | 159 | ... | ... | ... | ... | 950 | 138 | ... | ... | ... | ... | ... | ... | ... |
| IN-792 | 1170 | 150 | ... | ... | .... | ... | 1060 | 154 | ... | ... | ... | ... | 4 | ... | ... |
| M-22 | 730 | 106 | 780 | 113 | ... | ... | 685 | 99 | 730 | 106 | ... | ... | 5.5 | 4.5 | ... |
| MAR-M200 | 930 | 135 | 945 | 137 | 325 | 47 | 840 | 122 | 880 | 123 | ... | ... | 7 | 5 | ... |
| MAR-M246 | 965 | 140 | 1000 | 145 | 345 | 50 | 860 | 125 | 860 | 125 | ... | ... | 5 | 5 | ... |
| MAR-M247 | 965 | 140 | 1035 | 150 | ... | ... | 815 | 118 | 825 | 120 | ... | ... | 7 | ... | ... |
| MAR-M421 | 1085 | 157 | 995 | 147 | ... | ... | 930 | 135 | 815 | 118 | ... | ... | 4.5 | 3 | ... |
| MAR-M432 | 1240 | 180 | 1105 | 160 | ... | ... | 1070 | 155 | 910 | 132 | ... | ... | 6 | ... | ... |
| MC-102 | 675 | 98 | 655 | 95 | ... | ... | 605 | 88 | 540 | 78 | ... | ... | 5 | 9 | ... |
| Nimocast 75 | 500 | 72 | ... | ... | ... | ... | 179 | 26 | ... | ... | ... | ... | 39 | ... | ... |
| Nimocast 80 | 730 | 106 | ... | ... | ... | ... | 520 | 75 | ... | ... | ... | ... | 15 | ... | ... |
| Nimocast 90 | 700 | 102 | 595 | 86 | ... | ... | 520 | 75 | 420 | 61 | ... | ... | 14 | 15 | ... |
| Nimocast 242 | 460 | 67 | ... | ... | ... | ... | 300 | 44 | ... | ... | ... | ... | 8 | ... | ... |
| Nimocast 263 | 730 | 106 | ... | ... | ... | ... | 510 | 74 | ... | ... | ... | ... | 18 | ... | ... |
| Rene 77 | ... | ... | ... | ... | ... | ... | ... | ... | ... | ... | ... | ... | ... | ... | ... |
| Rene 80 | ... | ... | ... | ... | ... | ... | ... | ... | ... | ... | ... | ... | ... | ... | ... |
| Udimet 500 | 930 | 135 | 895 | 130 | ... | ... | 815 | 118 | 725 | 105 | ... | ... | 13 | 13 | ... |
| Udimet 710 | 1075 | 156 | ... | ... | 240 | 35 | 895 | 130 | ... | ... | 170 | 25 | 8 | ... | ... |
| CMSX-2(a) | 1185 | 172 | 1295(b) | 188(b) | ... | ... | 1135 | 165 | 1245(b) | 181(b) | ... | ... | 10 | 17(b) | ... |
| GMR-235 | 710 | 103 | ... | ... | ... | ... | 640 | 93 | ... | ... | ... | ... | 3 | ... | 18(b) |
| IN-939 | 1050 | 152 | 915(b) | 133(b) | 325(c) | 47(c) | 800 | 116 | 635(b) | 92(b) | 205(c) | 30(c) | 5 | 7(b) | 25(b) |
| MM 002(d) | 1035 | 150 | 1035(b) | 150(b) | 550(c) | 80(c) | 825 | 120 | 860(b) | 125(b) | 345(c) | 50(c) | 7 | 5(b) | 12(b) |
| IN-713 Hf(e) | 1000 | 145 | 895(b) | 130(b) | 380(c) | 55(c) | 760 | 110 | 620(b) | 90(b) | 240(c) | 35(c) | 11 | 6(b) | 20(b) |
| Rene 125 Hf(f) | 1070 | 155 | 1070(b) | 155(b) | 550(c) | 80(c) | 825 | 120 | 860(b) | 125(b) | 345(c) | 50(c) | 5 | 5(b) | 12(b) |
| MAR-M 246 Hf(g) | 1105 | 160 | 1070(b) | 155(b) | 565(c) | 82(c) | 860 | 125 | 860(b) | 125(b) | 345(c) | 50(c) | 6 | 7(b) | 14(b) |
| MAR-M 200 Hf(h) | 1035 | 150 | 1035(b) | 150(b) | 540(c) | 78(c) | 825 | 120 | 860(b) | 125(b) | 345(c) | 50(c) | 5 | 5(b) | 10(b) |
| PWA-1480(a) | ... | ... | 1130(b) | 164(b) | 685(c) | 99(c) | 895 | 130 | 905(b) | 131(b) | 495(c) | 72(c) | 4 | 8(b) | 20(b) |
| SEL | 1020 | 148 | 875(b) | 127(b) | ... | ... | 905 | 131 | 795(b) | 115(b) | ... | ... | 6 | 7(b) | ... |
| UDM 56 | 945 | 137 | 945(b) | 137(b) | ... | ... | 850 | 123 | 725(b) | 105(b) | ... | ... | 3 | 5(b) | ... |
| SEL-15 | 1060 | 154 | 1090(b) | 158(b) | ... | ... | 895 | 130 | 815(b) | 118(b) | ... | ... | 9 | 5(b) | ... |
| **Cobalt-base** | | | | | | | | | | | | | | | |
| AiResist 13(i) | 600 | 87 | 420(b) | 61(b) | ... | ... | 530 | 77 | 330(b) | 48(b) | ... | ... | 1.5 | 4.5(b) | ... |
| AiResist 215(i) | 690 | 100 | 570(j) | 83(j) | ... | ... | 485 | 70 | 315(j) | 46(j) | ... | ... | 4 | 12(j) | ... |
| FSX-414 | ... | ... | ... | ... | ... | ... | ... | ... | ... | ... | ... | ... | ... | ... | ... |
| Haynes 1002 | 770 | 112 | 560 | 81 | 115 | 17 | 470 | 68 | 345 | 50 | 95 | 14 | 6 | 8 | 28 |
| MAR-M 302 | 930 | 135 | 795 | 115 | 150 | 22 | 690 | 100 | 505 | 73 | 150 | 22 | 2 | ... | 21 |
| MAR-M 322(i) | 830 | 120 | 595(b) | 86(b) | ... | ... | 630 | 91 | 345(b) | 50(b) | ... | ... | 4 | 6.5(b) | ... |
| MAR-M 509 | 785 | 114 | 570 | 83 | ... | ... | 570 | 83 | 400 | 58 | ... | ... | 4 | 6 | ... |
| WI-52 | 750 | 109 | 745 | 108 | 160 | 23 | 585 | 85 | 440 | 64 | 105 | 15 | 5 | 7 | 35 |
| X-40 | 745 | 108 | 550 | 80 | ... | ... | 525 | 76 | 275 | 40 | ... | ... | 9 | 17 | ... |

(a) Single crystal [001]. (b) At 760 °C (1400 °F). (c) At 980 °C (1800 °F). (d) RR-7080. (e) MM 004. (f) M 005. (g) MM 006. (h) MM 009. (i) Data from Vol 3, 9th ed., *Metals Handbook*, 1980. (j) At 650 °C (1200 °F). Source: Nickel Development Institute, except as noted

## Table C.3 Stress-rupture strengths for selected wrought superalloys

| Alloy | Form | Rupture strength at: 650 °C (1200 °F) MPa | ksi | 760 °C (1400 °F) MPa | ksi | 870 °C (1600 °F) MPa | ksi | 980 °C (1800 °F) MPa | ksi |
|---|---|---|---|---|---|---|---|---|---|
| **Nickel-base** | | | | | | | | | |
| Astroloy | Bar | 770 | 112 | 425 | 62 | 170 | 25 | 55 | 8 |
| Cabot | ... | ... | ... | ... | ... | 30 | 4 | 15 | 2 |
| D-979 | Bar | 515 | 75 | 250 | 36 | 70 | 10 | ... | ... |
| Hastelloy S | Bar | ... | ... | 90 | 13 | 25 | 4 | ... | ... |
| Hastelloy X | Sheet | 215 | 31 | 105 | 15 | 40 | 6 | 15 | 2 |
| Haynes 230 | ... | ... | ... | 125 | 18 | 55 | 8 | 15 | 2 |
| Inconel 587 | Bar | ... | ... | 285 | 41 | ... | ... | ... | ... |
| Inconel 597 | Bar | ... | ... | 340 | 49 | ... | ... | ... | ... |
| Inconel 600 | Bar | ... | ... | ... | ... | 30 | 4 | 15 | 2 |
| Inconel 601 | Sheet | 195 | 28 | 60 | 9 | 30 | 4 | 15 | 2 |
| Inconel 617 | Bar | 360 | 52 | 165 | 24 | 60 | 9 | 30 | 4 |
| Inconel 617 | Sheet | ... | ... | 160 | 23 | 60 | 9 | 30 | 4 |
| Inconel 625 | Bar | 370 | 54 | 160 | 23 | 50 | 7 | 20 | 3 |
| Inconel 706 | Bar | 580 | 84 | ... | ... | ... | ... | ... | ... |
| Inconel 718 | Bar | 595 | 86 | 195 | 28 | ... | ... | ... | ... |
| Inconel 718 Direct Age | Bar | 405 | 59 | ... | ... | ... | ... | ... | ... |
| Inconel 718 Super | Bar | 600 | 87 | ... | ... | ... | ... | ... | ... |
| Inconel X750 | Bar | 470 | 68 | ... | ... | 50 | 7 | ... | ... |
| M-252 | Bar | 565 | 82 | 270 | 39 | 95 | 14 | ... | ... |
| Nimonic 75 | Bar | 170 | 25 | 50 | 7 | 5 | 1 | ... | ... |
| Nimonic 80A | Bar | 420 | 61 | 160 | 23 | ... | ... | ... | ... |
| Nimonic 90 | Bar | 455 | 66 | 205 | 30 | 60 | 9 | ... | ... |
| Nimonic 105 | Bar | ... | ... | 330 | 48 | 130 | 19 | 30 | 4 |
| Nimonic 115 | Bar | ... | ... | 420 | 61 | 185 | 27 | 70 | 10 |
| Nimonic 942 | Bar | 520 | 75 | 270 | 39 | ... | ... | ... | ... |
| Nimonic PE.11 | Bar | 335 | 49 | 145 | 21 | ... | ... | ... | ... |
| Nimonic PE.16 | Bar | 345 | 50 | 150 | 22 | ... | ... | ... | ... |
| Nimonic PK.33 | Sheet | 655 | 95 | 310 | 45 | 90 | 13 | ... | ... |
| Pyromet 860 | Bar | 545 | 79 | 250 | 36 | ... | ... | ... | ... |
| Rene 41 | Bar | 705 | 102 | 345 | 50 | 115 | 17 | ... | ... |
| Rene 95 | Bar | 860 | 125 | ... | ... | ... | ... | ... | ... |
| Udimet 400 | Bar | 600 | 87 | 305 | 44 | 110 | 16 | ... | ... |
| Udimet 500 | Bar | 760 | 110 | 325 | 47 | 125 | 18 | ... | ... |
| Udimet 520 | Bar | 585 | 85 | 345 | 50 | 150 | 22 | ... | ... |
| Udimet 700 | Bar | 705 | 102 | 425 | 62 | 200 | 29 | 55 | 8 |
| Udimet 710 | Bar | 870 | 126 | 460 | 67 | 200 | 29 | 70 | 10 |
| Udimet 720 | Bar | 670 | 97 | ... | ... | ... | ... | ... | ... |
| Unitemp AF2-1DA6 | Bar | 885 | 128 | 360 | 52 | ... | ... | ... | ... |
| Waspaloy | Bar | 615 | 89 | 290 | 42 | 110 | 16 | ... | ... |
| **Iron-base** | | | | | | | | | |
| A286 | Bar | 315 | 46 | 105 | 15 | ... | ... | ... | ... |
| Alloy 901 | Sheet | 525 | 76 | 205 | 30 | ... | ... | ... | ... |
| Discaloy | Bar | 275 | 40 | 60 | 9 | ... | ... | ... | ... |
| Haynes 556 | Sheet | 275 | 40 | 125 | 18 | 55 | 8 | 20 | 3 |
| Incoloy 800 | Bar | 165 | 24 | 66 | 9.5 | 30 | 4.4 | 13 | 1.9 |
| Incoloy 801 | Bar | ... | ... | ... | ... | ... | ... | ... | ... |
| Incoloy 802 | Bar | 170 | 25 | 110 | 16 | 69 | 10 | 24 | 3.5 |
| Incoloy 807 | Bar | ... | ... | 105 | 15 | 43 | 6.2 | 19 | 2.7 |
| Incoloy 903 | Bar | 510 | 74 | ... | ... | ... | ... | ... | ... |
| Incoloy 909 | Bar | 345 | 50 | ... | ... | ... | ... | ... | ... |
| N-155 | Bar | 295 | 43 | 140 | 20 | 70 | 10 | 20 | 3 |
| V-57 | Bar | 485 | 70 | ... | ... | ... | ... | ... | ... |
| **Cobalt-base** | | | | | | | | | |
| Haynes 188 | Sheet | ... | ... | 165 | 24 | 70 | 10 | 30 | 4 |
| L-605 | Sheet | 270 | 39 | 165 | 24 | 75 | 11 | 30 | 4 |
| MAR-M918 | Sheet | ... | ... | 60 | 9 | 20 | 3 | 5 | 1 |
| Haynes 150 | ... | ... | ... | 40(a) | 5.8 | ... | ... | ... | ... |

(a) At 815 °C (1500 °F)

## Table C.4 Stress-rupture strengths for selected cast superalloys

| Alloy | Rupture strength at: 815 °C (1500 °F) 100 h MPa (ksi) | 815 °C (1500 °F) 1000 h MPa (ksi) | 870 °C (1600 °F) 100 h MPa (ksi) | 870 °C (1600 °F) 1000 h MPa (ksi) | 980 °C (1800 °F) 100 h MPa (ksi) | 980 °C (1800 °F) 1000 h MPa (ksi) |
|---|---|---|---|---|---|---|
| **Nickel-base** | | | | | | |
| IN-713 LC | 425 (62) | 325 (47) | 295 (43) | 240 (35) | 140 (20) | 105 (15) |
| IN-713 C | 370 (54) | 305 (44) | 305 (44) | 215 (31) | 130 (19) | 70 (10) |
| IN-738 C | 470 (68) | 345 (50) | 330 (38) | 235 (34) | 130 (19) | 90 (13) |
| IN-738 LC | 430 (62) | 315 (46) | 295 (43) | 215 (31) | 140 (20) | 90 (13) |
| IN-100 | 455 (66) | 365 (53) | 360 (52) | 260 (38) | 160 (23) | 90 (13) |
| MAR-M 247 (MM 0011) | 585 (85) | 415 (60) | 455 (66) | 290 (42) | 185 (27) | 125 (18) |
| MAR-M 246 | 525 (76) | 435 (62) | 440 (63) | 290 (42) | 195 (28) | 125 (18) |
| MAR-M 246 Hf(MM 006) | 530 (77) | 425 (62) | 425 (62) | 285 (41) | 205 (30) | 130 (19) |
| MAR-M 200 | 495 (72) | 415 (60) | 385 (56) | 295 (43) | 170 (25) | 125 (18) |
| MAR-M 200 Hf(MM 009) | ... | ... | ... | 305 (44) | ... | 125 (18) |
| B-1900 | 510 (74) | 380 (55) | 385 (56) | 250 (36) | 180 (26) | 110 (16) |
| Rene 77 | ... | ... | 310 (45) | 215 (31.5) | 130 (19) | 62 (9.0) |
| Rene 80 | ... | ... | 350 (51) | 240 (35) | 160 (23) | 105 (15) |
| IN-625 | 130 (19) | 110 (16) | 97 (14) | 76 (11) | 34 (5) | 28 (4) |
| IN-162 | 505 (73) | 370 (54) | 340 (49) | 255 (37) | 165 (24) | 110 (16) |
| IN-731 | 505 (73) | 365 (53) | ... | ... | 165 (24) | 105 (15) |
| IN-792 | 515 (75) | 380 (55) | 365 (53) | 260 (38) | 165 (24) | 105 (15) |
| M-22 | 515 (75) | 385 (56) | 395 (57) | 285 (41) | 200 (29) | 130 (19) |
| MAR-M 421 | 450 (65) | 305 (44) | 310 (46) | 215 (31) | 125 (18) | 83 (12) |
| MAR-M 432 | 435 (63) | 330 (48) | 295 (40) | 215 (31) | 140 (20) | 97 (14) |
| MC-102 | 195 (28) | 145 (21) | 145 (21) | 105 (15) | ... | ... |
| Nimocast 90 | 160 (23) | 110 (17) | 125 (18) | 83 (12) | ... | ... |
| Nimocast 242 | 110 (16) | 83 (12) | 90 (13) | 59 (8.6) | 45 (6.5) | ... |
| Udimet 500 | 330 (48) | 240 (35) | 230 (33) | 165 (24) | 90 (13) | ... |
| Udimet 710 | 420 (61) | 325 (47) | 305 (44) | 215 (31) | 150 (22) | 76 (11) |
| CMSX-2 | ... | ... | ... | 345 (50) | ... | 170 (25) |
| GMR-235 | ... | ... | ... | 180 (26) | ... | 75 (11) |
| IN-939 | ... | ... | ... | 195 (28) | ... | 60 (9) |
| MM 002 | ... | ... | ... | 305 (44) | ... | 125 (18) |
| IN-713 Hf(MM 004) | ... | ... | ... | 205 (30) | ... | 90 (13) |
| Rene 125 Hf(MM 005) | ... | ... | ... | 305 (44) | ... | 115 (17) |
| SEL-15 | ... | ... | ... | 295 (43) | ... | 75 (11) |
| UDM 56 | ... | ... | ... | 270 (39) | ... | 125 (18) |
| **Cobalt-base** | | | | | | |
| HS-21 | 150 (22) | 95 (14) | 115 (17) | 90 (13) | 60 (9) | 50 (7) |
| X-40 (HS-31) | 180 (26) | 140 (20) | 130 (19) | 105 (15) | 75 (11) | 55 (8) |
| MAR-M 509 | 270 (39) | 225 (33) | 200 (29) | 140 (20) | 115 (17) | 90 (13) |
| FSX-414 | 150 (22) | 115 (17) | 110 (16) | 85 (12) | 55 (8) | 35 (5) |
| WI-52 | ... | 195 (28) | 172 (25) | 150 (22) | 90 (13) | 70 (10) |

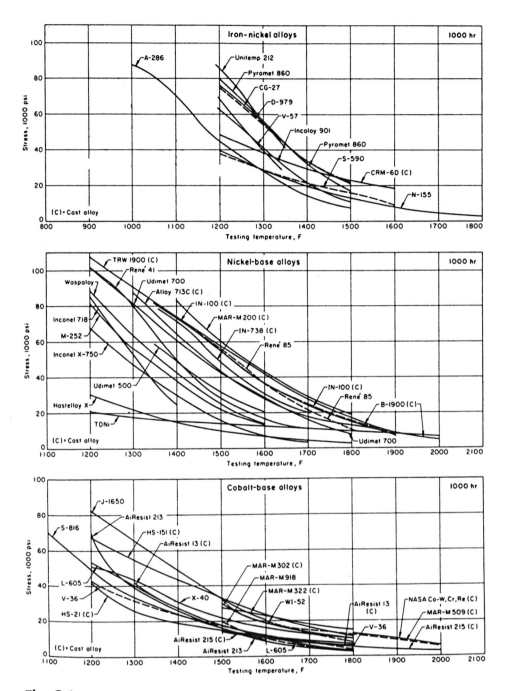

**Fig. C.1** 1000 h stress-rupture strength for each superalloy family. Source: Ref 1

## REFERENCE

1. M.J. Donachie and S.J. Donachie, *Superalloys: A Technical Guide*, 2nd ed., ASM International, 2002

APPENDIX **D**

# Micrograph Gallery

Comprising the Micrograph Gallery are selected nickel- and cobalt-base alloys that further illustrate microstructural features described in the book. These images were selected from the micrograph collection in the ASM Micrograph Center, which can be accessed through the ASM International website, www.asminternational.org. Interested readers can find expanded micrograph details and more images of superalloy microstructures in the Micrograph Center.

## REFERENCES

1. ASM Micrograph Center, http://products.asminternational.org/mgo/index.jsp
2. *Atlas of Microstructures of Industrial Alloys,* Vol 7, *Metals Handbook,* 8th ed., American Society for Metals, 1972, p157–192

# Alloy 718 (Nickel-base superalloy)

*UNS Number:* N07718
*Product Form:* Casting

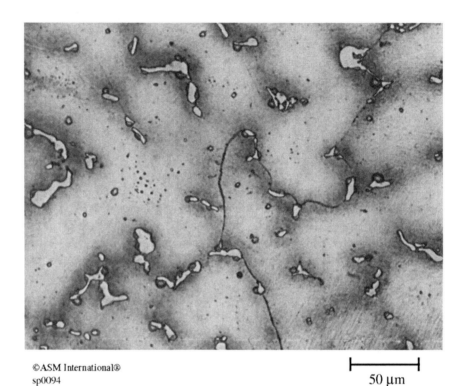

sp0094

|———————————————|
50 μm

**Fig. D.1** Laves phase (white islands) has precipitated at dendrites in the gamma matrix. Optical microscope, original magnification 250x.

*Condition:* Solution treated and aged—solution annealed 1 h at 1095 °C (2000 °F), air cooled, reannealed 1 h at 980 °C (1800 °F), air cooled, aged 16 h at 720 °C (1325 °F), air cooled. All furnace heating was done under a protective atmosphere of argon.

Source: Ref 1, 2

# Alloy 718 (Nickel-base superalloy)

*UNS Number:* N07718
*Product Form:* Casting (Vacuum cast)

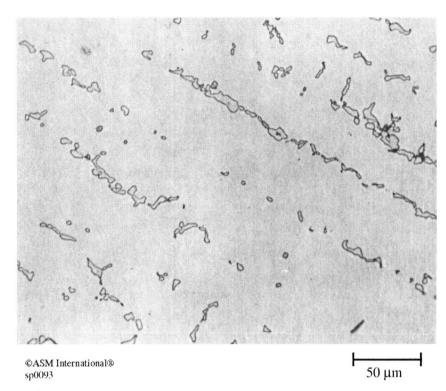

©ASM International®
sp0093

|⟵————————————⟶|
50 μm

**Fig. D.2** *Structure:* chainlike precipitate of M2(Cb,Ti). Laves phase in the gamma matrix. Optical microscope, original magnification 250x.

*Condition:* Heat treated (solution annealed 2 h at 1095 °C (2000 °F), air cooled, reannealed 1 h at 980 °C (1800 °F), air cooled, aged 16 h at 720 °C (1325 °F), air cooled)

Source: Ref 1, 2

# Alloy 718 (Nickel-base superalloy)

*UNS Number:* N07718
*Product Form:* Unspecified

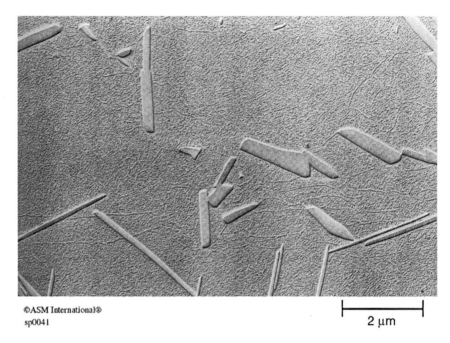

©ASM International®
sp0041

2 μm

**Fig. D.3** Details of delta phase crystals. Gamma prime precipitate is visible in the gamma matrix. Replica electron micrograph, original magnification 10,000×

*Condition:* Solution treated and aged—solution annealed 1 h at 955 °C (1750 °F), air cooled, aged 8 h at 720 °C (1325 °F), and furnace cooled in 10 h to 620 °C (1150 °F).

Source: Ref 1, 2

# Alloy 718 (Nickel-base superalloy)

*UNS Number:* N07718
*Product Form:* Unspecified

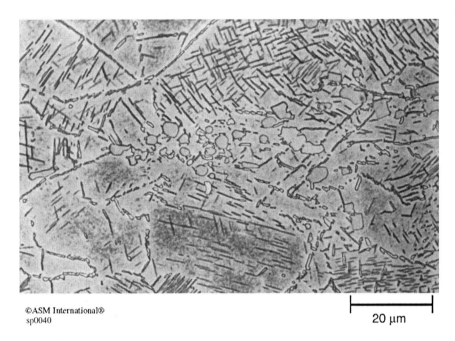

©ASM International®
sp0040

20 μm

**Fig. D.4** Structure is Laves phase (light gray particles), MC carbide (dark), and needlelike delta. The matrix is gamma phase. Optical microscope, original magnification 1000x.

*Condition:* Solution treated and aged—solution annealed 1 h at 955 °C (1750 °F), air cooled, and aged 10 h at 760 °C (1400 °F) and at 650 °C (1200 °F)

Source: Ref 1, 2

# Alloy 718 (Nickel-base superalloy)

*UNS Number:* N07718
*Product Form:* Unspecified

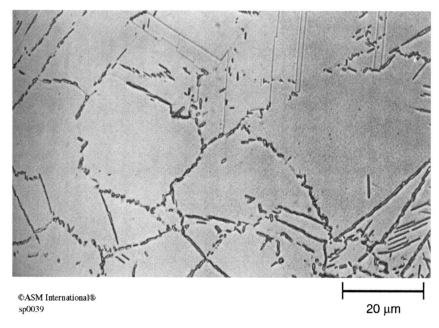

©ASM International®
sp0039

20 µm

**Fig. D.5** Structure is delta phase (Ni3Nb) in a gamma matrix. Optical microscope, original magnification 1000×.

*Condition:* Solution treated and aged—solution annealed 1 h at 955 °C (1750 °F),
air cooled, aged 8 h at 720 °C (1325 °F), and furnace cooled in 10 h to 620 °C
(1150 °F).

Source: Ref 1, 2

# Incoloy 901 (Nickel-base superalloy)

*UNS Number:* N09901
*Product Form:* Unspecified

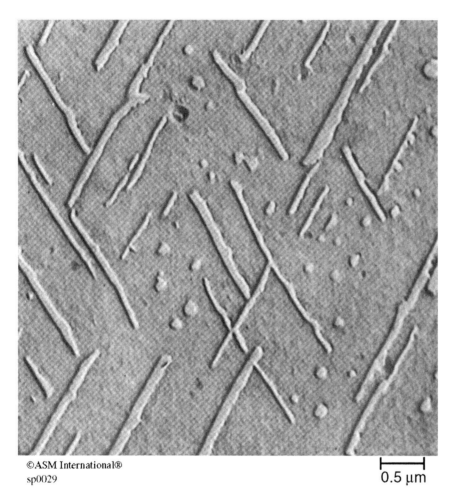

©ASM International®
sp0029

0.5 μm

**Fig. D.6** The needlelike constituent is eta phase (Ni3Ti); the remainder of the structure is gamma prime in a gamma matrix. Negative-replica electron micrograph, original magnification 15,000x.

*Condition:* Miscellaneous condition(s)—creep tested to rupture at 138 MPa (20 ksi) for 7380 h at 730 °C (1350 °F).

Source: Ref 1, 2

# Incoloy 901 (Nickel-base superalloy)

*UNS Number:* N09901
*Product Form:* Unspecified

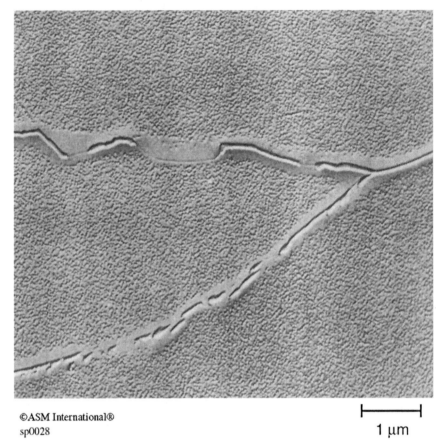

©ASM International®
sp0028

1 μm

**Fig. D.7** The grain-boundary constituents (MC, M3B2, or both) contributed to low ductility. Note the grain-boundary depleted zone. The gamma matrix contains gamma prime precipitate. Replica electron micrograph, original magnification 10,000×.

*Condition:* Heat treated—solution annealed 2 h at 1065 °C (1950 °F), water quenched, aged 2 h at 800 °C (1475 °F), air cooled, aged 24 h at 730 °C (1350 °F), and air cooled.

Source: Ref 1, 2

# Inconel X-750 (Nickel-base superalloy)

*UNS Number:* N07750
*Product Form:* Unspecified

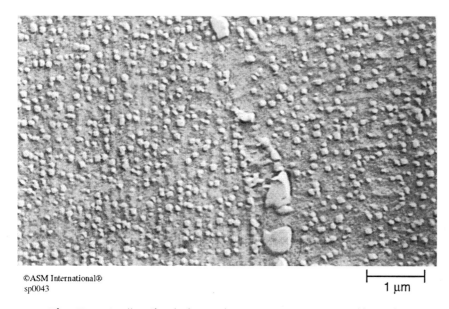

©ASM International®
sp0043

1 µm

**Fig. D.8** Small, uniformly dispersed gamma prime precipitate and large, discontinuous M23C6 carbide at the grain boundary. Replica electron micrograph, original magnification 15,000×.

*Condition:* Solution treated and aged—solution annealed 2 h at 1150 °C (2100 °F) and air cooled, then aged 24 h at 815 °C (1500 °F).

Source: Ref 1, 2

# Inconel X-750 (Nickel-base superalloy)

*UNS Number:* N07750
*Product Form:* Unspecified

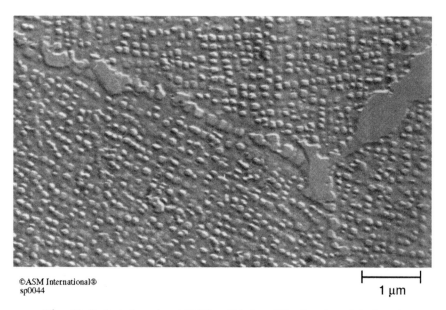

©ASM International®
sp0044

$\vdash\!\!\!\!-\!\!\!\!-\!\!\!\!\dashv$
1 μm

**Fig. D.9** Grain-boundary M23C6 carbide is stabilized, and precipitation of fine gamma prime particles has increased. Replica electron micrograph, original magnification 15,000×.

*Condition:* Solution treated and aged—solution annealed 2 h at 1150 °C (2100 °F) and air cooled, then aged 24 h at 845 °C (1550 °F), then 24 h at 705 °C (1300 °F).

Source: Ref 1, 2

# U-700 (Udimet) (Nickel-base superalloy)

*Product Form:* Forging

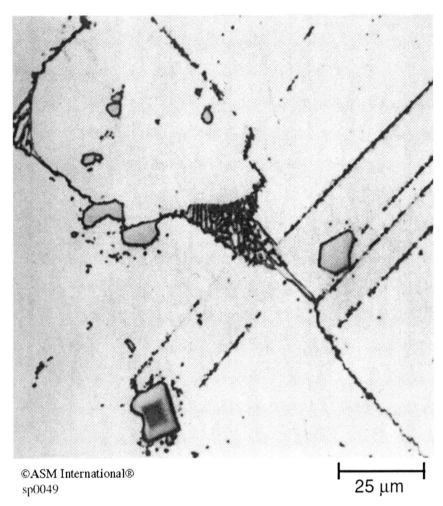

©ASM International®
sp0049

25 μm

**Fig. D.10** Nickel-rich solid-solution matrix, eutectic with M3B2 formed by fusion at 1205 °C (2200 °F), large crystals of metal carbide, and M23C6 carbide at grain and twin boundaries. Optical microscope, original magnification 500×.

*Condition:* As fabricated (as forged)

Source: Ref 1, 2

# U-700 (Udimet) (Nickel-base superalloy)

## *Product Form:* Forging

5 μm

**Fig. D.11** The lamellar constituent is a boride (M3B2) formed by incipient fusion. The two large crystals are metal carbide. Optical microscope, original magnification 1500×.

*Condition:* As fabricated (as forged)

Source: Ref 1, 2

# U-700 (Udimet) (Nickel-base superalloy)

*Product Form:* Unspecified

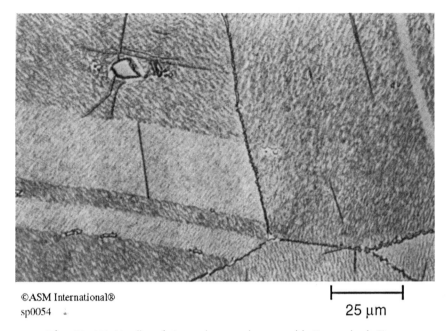

sp0054

25 µm

**Fig. D.12** Needles of sigma phase are longer and better resolved. Sigma formation adversely affects high-temperature tensile properties. Optical microscope, original magnification 500×.

*Condition:* Heat treated—solution annealed 4 h at 1175 °C (2150 °F), aged 4 h at 1080 °C (1975 °F), aged 24 h at 845 °C (1550 °F), and aged 16 h at 760 °C (1400 °F), then held 1500 h at 870 °C (1600 °F).

Source: Ref 1, 2

# U-700 (Udimet) (Nickel-base superalloy)

## *Product Form:* Unspecified

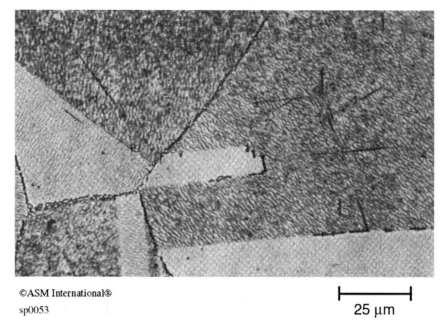

sp0053

|———————————|
25 µm

**Fig. D.13** Light, acicular sigma phase has formed in the gamma-gamma prime matrix; some sigma is also visible at boundaries of the platelets. Optical microscope, original magnification 500×.

*Condition:* Heat treated—solution annealed 4 h at 1175 °C (2150 °F), aged 4 h at 1080 °C (1975 °F), aged 24 h at 845 °C (1550 °F), and aged 16 h at 760 °C (1400 °F), then held 500 h at 870 °C (1600 °F).

Source: Ref 1, 2

# U-700 (Udimet) (Nickel-base superalloy)

**Product Form:** Unspecified

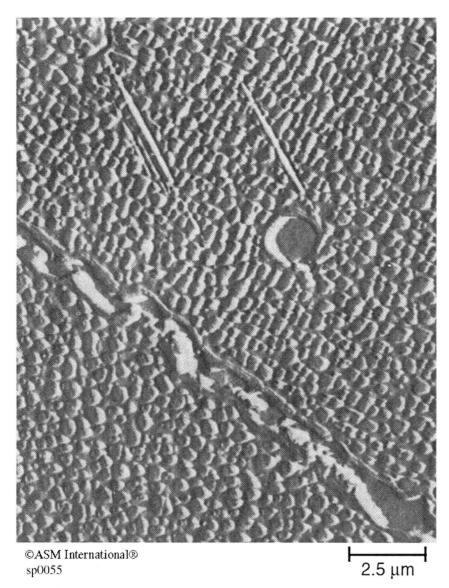

©ASM International®
sp0055

2.5 µm

**Fig. D.14** Structure is acicular sigma phase, M23C6 carbide at grain boundary, and gamma prime within the gamma matrix grains. Optical microscope, original magnification 4500×.

*Condition:* Solution treated and aged—solution annealed 4 h at 1175 °C (2150 °F) and aged 1500 h at 815 °C (1500 °F).

Source: Ref 1, 2

## U-700 (Udimet) (Nickel-base superalloy)

### *Product Form:* Unspecified

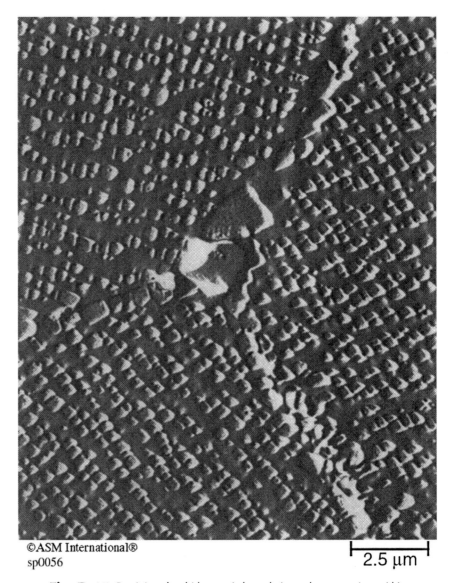

©ASM International®
sp0056

2.5 μm

**Fig. D.15** Precipitated carbide at grain boundaries and gamma prime within grains of the gamma solid-solution matrix. Replica electron micrograph, original magnification 4500×.

*Condition:* Solution treated and aged—solution annealed 4 h at 1175 °C (2150 °F) and aged 24 h at 980 °C (1800 °F).

Source: Ref 1, 2

# Haynes 25 (Cobalt-base superalloy)

*Alternate Name:* L-605
*UNS Number:* R30605
*Product Form:* Unspecified

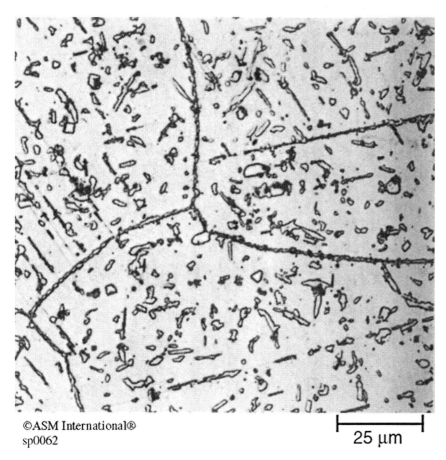

©ASM International®
sp0062

$\vdash$———————$\dashv$
25 μm

**Fig. D.16** Structure is precipitates of M6C and "Co2W" intermetallic in a face-centered cubic matrix. Optical microscope, original magnification 500×.

*Condition:* Solution treated and aged—solution annealed at 1205 °C (2200 °F) and aged 3400 h at 870 °C (1600 °F).

Source: Ref 1, 2

# Stellite 6B (Cobalt-base superalloy)

*UNS Number:* R30016
*Product Form:* Unspecified

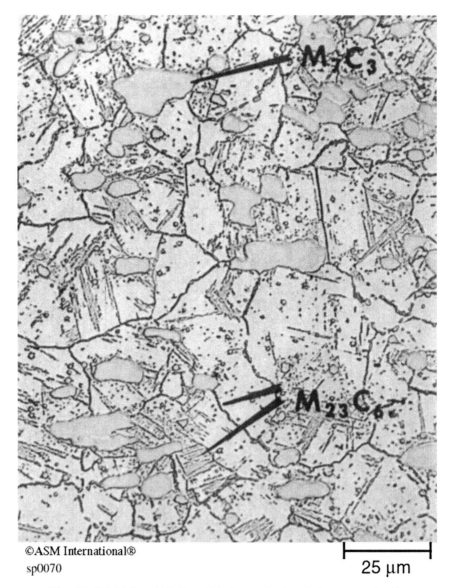

©ASM International®
sp0070

25 μm

**Fig. D.17** $M_7C_3$ and $M_{23}C_6$ carbides in a predominantly face-centered cubic matrix with some hexagonal close-packed crystals. Optical microscope, original magnification 500×.

*Condition:* Solution treated and aged—solution annealed at 1230 °C (2250 °F) and aged 8 h at 900 °C (1650 °F).

Source: Ref 1, 2

# Index

# C

face-centered cubic (fcc) matrix stabilizer,
61(T), 62(T), 63(T)
fcc austenite, 9
fluxing, 66, 73, 111
forging, 113–114
freckles, 82–83
freckling, 60, 72, 80, 83, 88

# G

gallium, 102
GAR. *See* grain aspect ratio (GAR)
gas turbine engines (GTEs). *See also*
  aircraft GTE
    air foils, 1
    alloys for applications where stress
     relaxation is to be avoided, 7
    alloys for components requiring critical
     clearance, 7
    ASTM 12, 27
    austenitic stainless steels, 3
    auxiliary components, 7
    "bowing" of the airfoil due to creep
     formation, 7
    casings, 7
    cobalt-base superalloys, 12
    combustor, 6
    combustor, alloys for, 6
    first self-sustaining, 3
    historical development, 3–4
    rotating parts, 6, 7
    stationary parts, 6–7
    superalloy applications, 6–7
    turbine blade applications, temperature
     ranges for superalloys in, 49(T)
    turbine blades, 7, 12
    turbine disks, 7
    turbine vanes, 7, 12
    U.S. Army, 3
    Waspaloy, 7
    wrought Rex-78, 4
gcp. *See* geometrically close-packed (gcp)
  phases
General Electric company, 3
General Electric turbosupercharger engine,
  3
geometrically close-packed (gcp) phases
  $\gamma'$-Ni$_3$(Al,Ti)

aluminum, 29
aluminum content in the $\gamma'$ phase, 32
chromium content in the $\gamma'$ phase, 32
coarsening process, 32
Cu$_3$Au (L1$_2$)-type structure, 29
disadvantage of, 27–28(T), 33
$\gamma'$ phase morphologies, 30(F)
$\gamma'$ precipitate, size of, 32
hardness versus particle diameter in a
  low-$\gamma'$-volume-fraction nickel-base
  superalloy, 32(F)
lattice mismatch, 31–32
niobium, 29
niobium content in the $\gamma'$ phase, 32
pure Ni$_3$Al, 29
tetragonal distortion, 29
titanium, 29
titanium content in the $\gamma'$ phase, 32
volume fraction, importance of,
  32–33
yield strength and temperature,
  relationship between, 32
$\gamma''$-Ni$_3$Nb, 33–34
introduction, 29
versus tcp phases, 29
germanium, 102
gold, 102
grain aspect ratio (GAR), 22(F)
grain boundaries
  alloy 600, 67
  alloy 690, 67
  borides, 39
  boron, 85–87, 88(F), 114
  carbides, effect of, 23–24
  carbon, 60, 87, 114
  cracking at, 46
  creep formation at, 46
  damage located at, 46
  diffusion at, 46
  dispersed carbides along, 25
  $\gamma'$-Ni$_3$(Al,Ti), effect of, 29, 30(F)
  grain aspect ratio (GAR), 22
  grain-boundary elements, 83–85(F)
  grain-boundary strengtheners, 115
  hafnium, 89, 90
  high- or low-angle grain boundaries, 47
  high- or low-angle grain boundaries in
   DS superalloys, 47

nitrogen plasma immersion ion
  implantation, 41

# O

ODS. *See* oxide-dispersion-strengthened
  (ODS) alloys
ODS superalloys
  examples, 14
  highest useful temperatures, 6
Orowan bowing, 21
orthorhombic AlYO₃ (yttrium-aluminum
  perovskite), 40
overaging, 45, 65
oxidation, resistance to, 112–113
  alumina formers, 112
  cerium, 113
  chromia formers, 112
  hafnium, 113
  lanthanum, 113
  precipitation-hardened alloys, 112–
    113
  rhenium, 112
  titanium, 112
  weight ratio of chromium to aluminum,
    112
  yttrium, 113
oxide garnet, 94
oxide pegs, 93
oxide scale adhesion, 93, 94, 95
oxide-dispersion-strengthened (ODS)
  alloys. *See also* oxides
  ceramics and, 21
  development of, 5
  fabrication methods, 21
  grain aspect ratio (GAR), 22(F)
  grain-boundary strengtheners, 21
  historical development, 5
  limitations on use of, 23
  MA- 760, 21
  MA alloys, 21–22
  MA-6000, 21
  Orowan bypassing mechanism, 21
  thoria, 22
  use of term, 14
  very high temperature applications, 22
  yttria, 22
  zone annealing, 22

oxides, 39–40(F)
  compositional effects, 95–96
  in nickel-chromium alloys, 96
  orthorhombic AlYO₃ (yttrium-
    aluminum perovskite), 40
  oxidation resistance, effect on, 96
  purpose of, 95
  strengthening and creep resistance in
    MA oxide-dispersion-strengthened
    (ODS) alloys, 95
  tetragonal Y₃Al₅O₁₂ (yttrium-aluminum
    garnet), 40
  ThO₂, 39–40(F)
  uniform distribution of, 95–96
  Y₂O₃, 39–40(F)
  yttrium oxide (Y₂O₃), 95

# P

pack diffusion process, 87, 88(F)
periodic table, 59(F)
PHACOMP, 43
phases
  borides (*see* borides)
  carbides (*see* carbides)
  geometrically close-packed (gcp),
    29–34(F,T)
  introduction, 25–28(F,T)
  matrix phase, 28
  nickel-base superalloys, 27(F)
  nitrides (*see* nitrides)
  oxides (*see* oxides)
  sulfocarbides, 41
  in superalloys, 26–27(T)
  topologically close-packed (tcp) phases,
    41–43
phosphorus
  alloy 718, 101
  creep life, effect on, 101
  creep resistance, effect on, 101–102
  synergistic effect with boron, 101
pigtail constriction, 47
plain stainless steel, cost versus
  superalloys, 1
plasma-assisted processing, 41
porosity, 23–24, 84, 88, 99, 115
potassium, 102
powder metallurgy, 6, 14, 21, 27, 95, 98(F)

optimal rhenium levels for creep life
in second-generation single-crystal
superalloy, 73(T)
solid-solution hardening (SSH), 18
turbine blades
alloys for, 7
applications in GTE, 7
temperature ranges for superalloys in
turbine blade applications, 49(T)
turbine vanes
alloys for, 7
applications in GTE, 7
cobalt, use in, 66
type I hot corrosion, 67, 112
type II hot corrosion, 67, 73–74, 86, 112

## U

UC01, approximate solvus temperature of
$\gamma'$ for, 44(T)
Udimet 500
approximate solvus temperature of $\gamma'$
for, 44(T)
effect of boron and zirconium on creep
of, 84(T)
influence of oxygen content on the
stress-rupture life of, 98(F)
main oxide constituent of protective
oxide scale for selected superalloy,
68(T)
turbine blades, 7
Udimet 630, 13
Udimet 700, 7, 13
Udimet 700 (cast), approximate solvus
temperature of $\gamma'$ for, 44(T)
Udimet 700 (wrought), approximate solvus
temperature of $\gamma'$ for, 44(T)
Udimet 710, 86
$\gamma/\gamma'$ partitioning ratios, 74(T)
Udimet 720, 13, 86
UM-F13, 82(T)
United Aircraft Corporation, 5
United States, aircraft GTE, development
of, 4
Unitemp-718, 102(F)
uranium, 102
U.S. Army, 3

## V

V-57, strengthened through $\gamma'$ precipitation,
10
vacuum arc melting, 114
vacuum arc remelting, 4
vacuum casting, 4–5, 71
vacuum induction melting (VIM), 4, 114
void formation, 46
voids, 71, 96

## W

Waspaloy, 13
approximate solvus temperature of $\gamma'$
for, 44(T)
heat treatment, 46(T)
main oxide constituent of protective
oxide scale for selected superalloy,
68(T)
turbine disks, 7
turbine vanes, 7
Waspaloy, cobalt-reduced, 64
wear-resistant surfaces, 4
welding, 13, 21, 39, 70, 100
alloy 718, increasing weldability of,
103
Hastelloy X, increasing weldability of,
103
sulfur content effect on, 100
weldability assessment diagram for
superalloys, 71(F)
Widmanstätten structures, 26–27(T), 34,
38, 43(F)
wrought cobalt-base alloys, 34, 66, 70
wrought nickel-base superalloys, 13

## X

X-40
main oxide constituent of protective
oxide scale for selected superalloy,
68(T)
overview, 12
turbine vane assembly, 7
turbine vanes, 7

LaVergne, TN USA
07 December 2010
207648LV00002B/1/P

GAYLORD